PRENTICE-HALL ELECTRICAL ENGINEERING SERIES

WILLIAM L. EVERITT, *Editor*

Signal Flow Graphs and Applications

Louis P. A. Robichaud
Research Analyst
Canadian Armament Research and
Development Establishment
Lecturer, Laval University

Maurice Boisvert
Professor
Department of
Electrical Engineering
Laval University

Jean Robert
Associate Professor
Department of
Electrical Engineering
Laval University

Prentice-Hall, Inc.   Englewood Cliffs, N. J.
1962

PRENTICE-HALL INTERNATIONAL
London • *Tokyo* • *Sydney* • *Paris*
PRENTICE-HALL OF CANADA, LTD.
PRENTICE-HALL DE MEXICO, S.A.

Library of Congress Catalog Card Number 62–15497
Printed in the United States of America
89841—C

Foreword

The content of this monograph on Signal Flow Graphs is a result of research done at Laval University in the Department of Electrical Engineering.

The work of S. J. Mason on this subject suggested to one of the authors, M. Boisvert, material for a course given in 1954 in the Department of Electrical Engineering. The first two chapters resume the material of this course.

One of his research assistants, L. P. A. Robichaud from the Canadian Armament Research and Development Establishment, undertook a more profound study of flow graphs and their applications. His interesting work is presented in the following chapters: Direct Analysis of Electrical Networks, Algebra of Quadripole and N-port Networks, Direct Simulation on an Analogue Computer, Algebraic Reduction of Flow Graphs Using a Digital Computer.

In most Electrical Engineering Curricula, several courses are given to power and electronic engineering students in common in order to show them the basic unity of the methods applied to both branches. Flow graphs are a noteworthy example of this unity. The third author, J. Robert, shows in Chapter Six that flow graphs lend themselves well to the study of power engineering: Application of Signal Flow Graphs to Electrical Machine Theory, completed after consultation with L. P. A. Robichaud, who has given the course in Flow Graphs since 1957.

I wish to thank J. C. Gille, visiting professor in our Department, who encouraged this publication.

I congratulate the authors for this contribution to the field of Electrical Engineering.

Lionet Boulet, Head,
Department of
Electrical Engineering,
Faculty of Sciences,
Laval University

Preface

A major preoccupation of modern engineering concerns the study of lumped parameter physical systems. These systems consist of a network of physical elements defined by constant or variable parameters and possess a finite number of degrees of freedom. Electrical networks, linear servomechanisms, mechanical, electro-mechanical and electro-accoustical systems are typical examples. The engineer depicts these systems by schematic diagrams or networks, whose branches represent the physical elements. From such diagrams are derived the equations of the system which are generally integro-differential equations. At least in the linear case, these can be reduced with the help of Fourier and Laplace transforms to a set of algebraic equations.

One then proceeds with the reduction of the equations. The objectives of this reduction are either to obtain reduced systems of equations, which contain only certain variables of interest, or characteristic equations, or else to find certain relationships between the variables at the input and the output of the system, such as gains, input and transfer functions, and so on. Since the time of Cayley, Hamilton and Sylvester, matrix algebra has undoubtedly remained a powerful tool for the analysis of physical systems. Of particular note is the work of Kron (1) who thoroughly systematized the formulation of electrical network problems by using connection matrices to describe the network itself, and branch matrices to represent the elements which are interconnected to form the system.

The fact remains, however, that the equilibrium equations of a
system are essentially quantitative relations between the variables
and do not show explicitly the structure of the system under study.
However, the whole algebra of reduction of the system of equations
depends much more on this structure, that is on the interconnections of the elements, than on the nature of the elements themselves. The equations alone do not generally allow one to infer easily
certain fundamental relations or to make simplifications, whereas
the topology of the diagram suggests these immediately. Indeed,
who would think of using Thevenin's theorem to solve a system of
algebraic equations for one of the variables if he had not previously
seen the network corresponding to these equations?

Special techniques have been developed for the solution of some
physical systems. In practice, these techniques are generally restricted to well-defined domains, although in general they could be
translated into analogous problems in different fields. One can
mention in particular the techniques of analysis of electrical networks. In several problems of this type, one can go from an original
network to equivalent networks containing less and less branches,
and finally to an equivalent network from which the expression of
the desired variable can be obtained directly by inspection. It is
then unnecessary to write equations, and the process of algebraic
reduction with equivalent circuits frequently represents a consider-
able economy of effort when compared with matrix methods. If the
schematic diagrams show the functional relations in an explicit
enough manner, and if there exist techniques to perform the reduction of the diagram while maintaining some relationships invariant, one can use the name 'graphic algebra' to describe the
algebraic reduction performed with the help of equivalent networks. Another example of graphic algebra is found in the theory
of servomechanisms with its block diagrams. In these diagrams,
the functional relations are represented in a manner more explicit
even than in electric networks; it is thus not surprising to see
Tustin (2), for example, evaluate the determinant of a control
system by a simple enumeration of the loops in the block-diagram.

Mason's signal flow graphs (3) constitute certainly the most
advanced form of graphic algebra. In creating this type of graph,
Mason has made the node and the branch essentially pure representations of the variable and the functional relation. By divorcing the

idea of branch from the idea of physical element which was attached to any branch in the diagrams used until now, Mason has obtained a graph of the equations applicable to any field of engineering. In such problems, the independent variables represent excitations which are applied to the system, and the responses of the system are associated with the dependent variables. Signal flow graphs, as the name implies, depict the variables as signals traveling along the branches of the graph. These signals are modified according to the characteristics of the branches traversed. The incoming signals are added at each node to define a dependent variable which is considered as a new signal transmitted along all the branches starting from this node. Mason has shown that the topological transformations performed on linear graphs correspond to algebraic transformations performed on the system of equations. In this way, it is possible either to solve the graph directly, or to transform the graph into a residual form, in which appear only the nodes corresponding to specified variables or the branches representing the input and transfer functions of the system.

The use of signal flow graphs for the study of physical systems, especially systems represented by a schematic diagram, constitutes the objective of this monograph. The authors do not pretend to exhaust the subject or to cover all the applications of flow graphs; they have simply collected under the same title different investigations which were related to the study of linear systems with signal flow graphs.

In general, there are several ways of choosing the variables in a complex system. Corresponding to each choice, a system of equations can be written and each system of equations can be represented in a graph. This formulation of the equations becomes direct and automatic if one has at his disposal techniques which permit the drawing of a graph directly from the schematic diagram of the system under study. The structure of the graphs thus obtained is related in a simple manner to the topology of the schematic diagram, and it becomes unnecessary to consider the equations, even implicity, to obtain the graph. In some cases, one has simply to imagine the flow graph in the schematic diagram and the desired answers can be obtained without even drawing the flow graph.

The techniques developed in this monograph are useful particularly in problems defined by a schematic diagram, and their usefulness increases as the schematic diagram becomes more explicit. For this reason, and also possibly because of professional inclination, the authors have chosen to present this monograph in terms of electrical network theory, and to select as examples almost exclusively networks constructed of ideal transformers, active elements and gyrators, besides passive reciprocal elements. All the physical systems analogous to these networks constitute the domain of application of the techniques developed in the following chapters. Trent (4) has shown that all the physical systems which satisfy the following conditions fall into this category.

1. The finite lumped system is composed of a number of simple parts, each of which has known dynamical properties which can be defined by equations using two types of scalar variables and parameters of the system. Variables of the first type represent quantities which can be measured, at least conceptually, by attaching an indicating instrument to two connection points of the element. Variables of the second type characterize quantities which can be measured by connecting a meter in series with the element. Relative velocities and positions, pressure differentials and voltages are typical quantities of the first class, whereas electric currents, forces, rates of heat flow, are variables of the second type. Firestone (5) has been the first to distinguish these two types of variables with the names "across variables" and "through variables."

2. Variables of the first type must obey a mesh law, analogous to Kirchhoff's voltage law, whereas variables of the second type must satisfy an incidence law analogous to Kirchhoff's current law.

3. Physical dimensions of appropriate products of the variables of the two types must be consistent.

For the systems in which these conditions are satisfied, it is possible to draw a linear graph isomorphic with the dynamical properties of the system as described by the chosen variables. The techniques described in this monograph can be applied directly to these linear graphs as well as to electrical networks, to obtain a signal flow graph of the system.

The first two chapters present the elements of signal flow graph theory as developed by Mason. The method of presentation in Chapt. 2, in which the formal theory of feedback is briefly reviewed, stresses the relation between the closed path in the flow graph and the loop in feedback systems. Chapter 3 is entitled: "Direct analysis of electrical networks through signal flow graphs." It is shown in this chapter that one can consider elementary graphs corresponding to the branches of the network and that the elementary graphs can be interconnected in the same way that the elements of the networks are interconnected, or in the dualistic way, to produce a flow graph of the node or mesh equations. A closed path of two branches constitutes the elementary graph, and the functional relations represented by these branches depend directly on the impedance or the admittance of the corresponding branch in the network. A new formula is also developed for the expansion of the determinant of the graph in terms of the elements of the network. For passive networks without mutual inductances, this formula gives the same results as Kirchhoff's rules with its enumeration of all the trees; the new formula can however be applied to the flow graph of any network. In Chapt. 4, more complex elementary graphs are introduced; these have four branches and correspond to two-terminal-pair networks. Instead of a very detailed graph of the network, one obtains a condensed flow graph for a large network by interconnecting the elementary graphs in the same manner as the two-terminal-pair networks are connected to form the larger network. The description of this chapter remains close to the matrix formalism of quadripole theory. Flow graphs are, however, more flexible than matrices, since graphs corresponding to matrices of different forms can be joined together without first performing the transformations which are required before matrix addition or multiplication. The extension of these techniques to n-port networks is briefly mentioned. The simulation of a physical system on an analogue computer is treated in Chapt. 5. By choosing the elementary flow graphs of the preceeding chapter to correspond to the operational units of a computer, the signal flow graph itself can be used to set up the analogue. Because the graph is obtained directly from the schematic diagram of the physical system, this process can be called direct simulation, since it is not required to write the equations in order to set up the computer model. In Chapt. 6, the methods developed in Chapts. 4 and 5 are used in some examples drawn from the field of electrical machine theory; in particular flow graphs are used exclusively to study the generalized rotating machine. In any complex problem, if nu-

Contents

1

Elementary Theory

1-1 INTRODUCTION

"One might say that the problem of system analysis is a problem of handling simultaneous equations. This description is certainly valid but incomplete in that it fails to show how important gross identifications can be made in the system by inference from the equations themselves." To illustrate this remark of Linvill[6] one can refer to the theory of feedback, or to the issue of the IRE transactions on circuit theory devoted to signal theory[7]. It might be added to this first consideration that the similarity of two problems does not depend in the first place on the physical arrangement of the elements or on the dimensions of the variables, but rather on the structure of the relationships between the variables in the two problems. As a proof of such a statement, it is necessary only to recall the use of duality in network theory or the numerous overlappings in the theories of feedback and servomechanism. The frequent use by the electrical engineer of diagrams to represent the structure of the relations between the variables of a system, or certain fundamental relationships, is not surprising.

1

Although Mason, in developing signal flow graphs, has had constantly in mind the theory of feedback and has been profoundly influenced by Bode[8], these graphs have been extremely useful in all sorts of problems where feedback was not of particular interest. For this reason, only the elementary properties of signal flow graphs will be described in this chapter, leaving all the feedback aspects for a second chapter.

After the flow graph has been defined, it is shown that such a graph can be drawn at least as easily as the equations are formulated for a specific problem. A proper terminology will then be introduced to allow a simple statement of a few rules which will permit either the direct solution of the graph for a given variable; or the reduction of the graph to a residual form showing only certain fundamental relations; or the transformation of the graph by inversion of the relations between one excitation and one response.

1-2 DEFINITION OF SIGNAL FLOW GRAPHS

A signal flow graph *is a graph of directed branches, interconnected at certain points called nodes, defining uniquely a system of linear algebraic equations.* The **nodes** represent the variables and the coefficients of the equations are written alongside the branches and called **branch transmittances.** The variable x_j represented by the node j in the graph is then defined as the sum of all the products $t_{ij}x_i$ where t_{ij} is the transmittance of a branch going from node i to node j, and x_i is the variable at the node of origin of that branch. With the following system of equations:

$$\begin{aligned} x_2 &= ax_1 + bx_3 \\ x_3 &= x_0 + ex_1 + dx_2 \end{aligned} \tag{1-1}$$

where x_1 and x_0 are independent variables, the graph of Fig. 1-1a is obtained from the first equation and that of Figure 1-1b from the second. The complete graph for the Eq. (1-1) is shown in Fig. 1-1c.

Mason[3] compares this type of graph to a system of signal transmission in which the nodes of the independent variables are transmitting stations and the other nodes are repeaters. The signals travel along the branches and are modified by the transmittances of the branches traversed. The repeater at a given node combines all the incoming signals and sends the resulting signal along all the branches diverging from that node. From this analogy have come the names

(a)

(b)
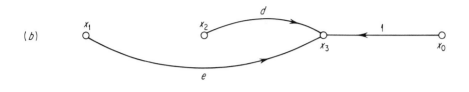

(c)
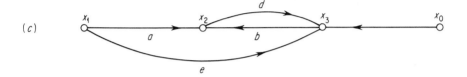

(d)
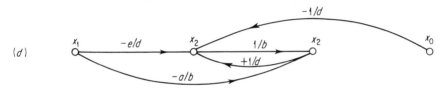

Fig. 1-1. Drawing of a flow graph

"signal flow graph" for this diagram and "transmittance" for the coefficient associated with a branch.

The signal flow graph contains the same information as the equations from which it is derived; but there does not exist a one-to-one correspondence between the graph and the system of equations. One system will give different graphs according to the order in which the equations are used to define the variable written on the left-hand side. As an example, by interchanging the Eq. (1-1) to define x_2 and x_3, one obtains the graph of Fig. 1-1d which contains the same information as that of Fig. 1-1c, but which is topologically different. With respect to the transmission of signals, this flexibility of flow graphs permits a representation very close to the physical system if the graph is drawn in such a way that the signal transmission corresponds directly to a physical phenomenon.

One notes that the signal flow graph is almost the same type of representation as the *block diagram* used in the theory of servo-mechanisms. However, the idea of branch is now generalized and completely divorced from the idea of block or group of physical elements usually present inside the blocks of a block diagram. In fact, the same physical element can appear in the transmittances of several branches of the flow graph as later examples will show.

The preceding definition of signal flow graph is really the definition of a linear graph. More generally, a flow graph, as defined originally by Mason[3], implies a set of functional relations, linear or not. However, for the applications considered in this monograph (except for a few particular examples) the definition of linear graph is sufficient and is the one used because it allows a simple algebra. The variables of the graph are then defined by linear equations of the form:

$$x_k = f_k(x_1, x_2, x_3, ..., x_n) \qquad (1\text{-}2)$$

or else are independent variables. The matrix T of the branch transmittances is a square matrix of order n equal to the number of nodes of the form:

$$T = \begin{vmatrix} t_{11} & t_{21} & t_{31} & ... \\ t_{12} & ... & ... & \\ ... & ... & ... & \\ t_{1n} & t_{2n} & t_{3n} & ... \end{vmatrix} \qquad (1\text{-}3)$$

and its elements are the derivatives:

$$t_{jk} = \frac{df_k}{dx_j} \qquad (1\text{-}4)$$

All the elements of a row k will be equal to zero if x_k is an independent variable. If one writes X for the column matrix of the variables $x_1, x_2, ..., x_n$, and φ for the column matrix of dependent variables ($\varphi_k = x_k - f_k$), one has for the system of equations represented in the flow graph:

$$(U - T)X = \varphi \qquad (1\text{-}5)$$

where U is the unit matrix of order n.

1-3 THE DRAWING OF THE FLOW GRAPH

The flow graph can always be obtained from a set of equations. It is necessary only to write the equations in the form shown in Eq. (1-2) with the dependent variables on the left-hand side, taking care to define all the dependent variables and to define them once only.

The usefulness of flow graphs is evidently greater if they can be drawn from a schematic diagram or from an equivalent circuit without the necessity of first writing the equations explicitly. This is always possible for electric networks, and the frequent use of the theorem of superposition is of great help in setting up the graph.

Examples are given in Fig. 1-2; in 1-2a and 1-2b, the flow graph is obtained in a step-by-step procedure to define the variables. In the circuit of Fig. 1-2c, one can consider the voltage e_k as an independent source and use the following superposition. With $e_k = 0$, the sources e_1 and e_2 give the output voltage e_{01} and e_{02} respectively, according to the formula of a grounded cathode amplifier:

$$A_i = - \frac{\mu_i R_{L_i}}{r_{p_i} + R_{L_i}} \qquad (i = 1, 2)$$

With the voltage e_k acting alone, the output voltages e_{01} and e_{02} are obtained by the gain formula of a grounded grid amplifier:

$$G_i = \frac{(1 + \mu_i) R_{L_i}}{r_{p_i} + R_{L_i}} \qquad (i = 1, 2)$$

(Instead of a single branch of transmittance G, one could draw a partial flow graph such as the one obtained in Fig. 1-2a). The voltage e_k is then defined from the current in R_k. In the example of Fig. 1-2d, a graph is first obtained for the passive part of the circuit including the admittance g_m of the tube, and then a branch is added to account for the contribution of the current source $- g_m e_1$ to the output current.

It can be seen from these examples that the subjective appreciation of the problem will have a great effect on the drawing of the flow graph for a physical system. It is evident that the choice of the variables and the equations leads to great flexibility, and that the order in which the nodes appear in the graph is of little significance. This flexibility also allows one to obtain a condensed graph showing only certain fundamental relations with the help of elaborate transfer functions, as in the example of Fig. 1-2c, or a detailed graph containing all the variables of the problem as in Fig. 1-2b. The reader can surely find other graphs for these same examples.

In the following chapters, methods will be presented to obtain a graph for a given system in a very direct manner, either by the choice of a topology of the graph which is directly related to the geometry of the system under study, or by a combination of elementary flow graphs corresponding to the elementary structures of the physical system.

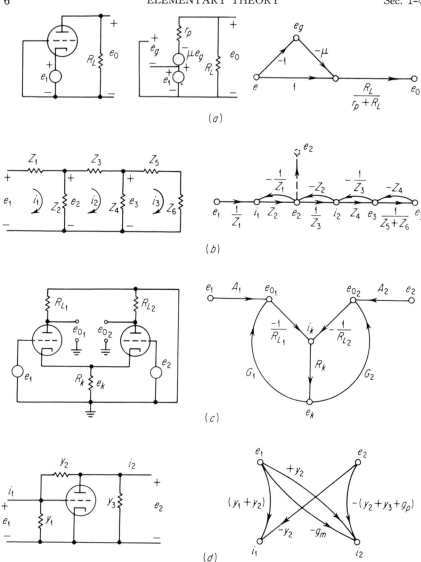

Fig. 1-2. Examples of signal flow graphs

1-4 DEFINITIONS AND TERMINOLOGY

The traversal of one or more successive branches in the direction indicated on the branches constitutes a **path.** A path is indicated either by enumeration of the branches traversed, as the path *a-d-b* in Fig. 1-1a, or by enumeration of the nodes along the path, as x_1-x_2-

x_3-x_2 for the path mentioned above. A path is called *open* if any node is not crossed more than once. If the nodes of the graph are numbered or follow a given order, one can distinguish a **direct path**, in which all successive nodes are of higher order, and an **inverse path** for the opposite case. Direct and inverse paths are necessarily open paths. The path i_1-e_2-i_2-e_3-i_3 in Fig. 1-2b is an example of direct path and i_3-e_3-i_2-e_2-i_1 constitutes an inverse path.

A *path starting at a node and terminating at the same node and in which any other node does not appear more than once is called a* **closed path** *or a* **loop**. In the example of Fig. 1-2c, one of the loops is the path e_{01}-i_k-e_k-e_{01}.

The **transmittance of an open path or of a closed path (loop)** *is the product of the transmittances of the branches of that path.* For the open path from e_1 to e_{02} in Fig. 1-2c, the transmittance is $A_1(- R_k / R_{L_1}) G_2$, whereas the loop at the node e_{01} in the same figure has a transmittance $- G_1 R_k / R_{L_1}$.

A node having only outgoing branches is called a **source** of the graph and must necessarily represent an *independent variable*. A node with only incoming branches is a **sink**. Since any dependent variable can be chosen as a sink, it is possible to add a sink in the graph by adding an extra node with a branch of unit transmittance, as shown by the dotted part in Fig. 1-2b. Nodes other than sources and sinks are internal nodes. A node can also be called *contributive* if there is a single outgoing branch and several incoming branches, or *distributive* in the opposite case[9]. In the graph of Fig. 1-2c, the nodes i_k and e_k are examples of contributive and distributive nodes, respectively.

Signal flow graphs can generally be divided into **cascade graphs** and **feedback graphs**. The cascade graph contains no loops, as in the example of Fig. 1-2c. Feedback graphs have one or more loops. Feedback analysts will have, no doubt, noticed a relation between feedback and the closed path of flow graphs, and thus it might appear surprising that the graph for the circuit of Fig. 1-2d has no loops. To this, one can answer with Mason that the mathematical concept of feedback exists only in the way the mind works a given problem. If one perceives a closed chain of relations between the variables of a given problem, it might be said that it is a feedback problem and the graph corresponding to this interpretation of the problem will be a feedback graph. The second chapter in this monograph will discuss the relations between feedback and flow graph.

Two nodes will be said to be coupled, if they are in the same loop. **A loop subgraph** is the set of all the nodes coupled together in a graph, with the branches joining these nodes. The simplest loop subgraph is the closed path consisting of a single branch which will be called a **self-loop**. The complexity of a given graph is measured by the **index** of the graph. *The index is defined as the minimum number of nodes which have to be split in order to remove all the loops in the graph. Splitting a node* means interrupting the transmission of signal at that node; it corresponds to the splitting of the node into two half nodes, one of these half nodes being a sink and the other being a source. In Fig. 1-3, two nodes are split and this removes all the loops; thus the index is two for this graph. One can verify that the index of the graph in Fig. 1-2c is one, whereas the graph in Fig. 1-2b has an index of two.

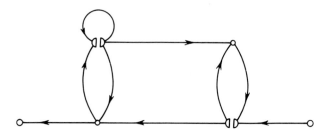

Fig. 1-3. Determination of the index

The nodes which are split to determine the index are called *index nodes* and in general the choice of these nodes is not unique. In Fig. 1-2b, either the node i_k or the node e_k can be chosen as index node. It is to be noted that the complexity of a graph depends not only on the number of loops, but also on the degree of coupling between the loops, and that the index permits a precise characterization of this complexity. This fact is of some importance in problems of feedback or control, and for the study of stability.

1-5 REDUCTION OF THE FLOW GRAPH

The algebra of linear flow graphs offers great flexibility for the algebraic reduction of a given problem. One can, for example, obtain the solution in a very direct manner, using Mason's rule, by writing directly the expression of a dependent variable in terms of independent variables simply by inspection of the graph and enumeration of sets of loops and open paths. Sometimes a reduction of the graph to some essential elements is preferred to a direct solution. This is generally the case in feedback and control problems in which it is desired to show explicitly transfer functions of certain parts of the system and control loops, or to study the effect of a parameter on the system.

The reduction of a graph proceeds by the elimination of certain nodes to obtain a *residual graph* showing only the variables of interest. This elimination of nodes is called "**node absorption.**" This method is close to the familiar process of successive eliminations of undesired variables in a system of equations. One can eliminate a variable by removing the corresponding node in the graph. If one reduces the graph sufficiently, it is possible to obtain the solution for any variable and this is the objective which will be kept in mind in this description of the different methods of reduction of the graph. In practice, however, the techniques of reduction will be used solely to transform the graph to a residual graph expressing some fundamental relationships. Complete solutions will be more easily obtained by application of Mason's rule.

The graph itself programs the reduction process. Indeed, a simple

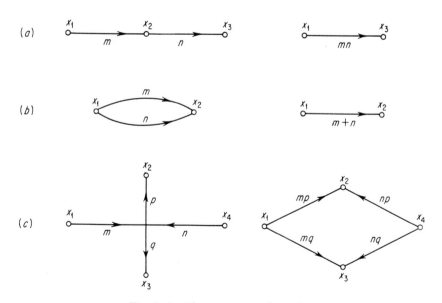

Fig. 1-4. Elementary transformations

inspection of the graph readily suggests the different steps of the reduction which are carried out by elementary transformations, by loop elimination, or by the use of a reduction formula.

1) **The elementary transformations** are shown in Fig. 1-4 and can be proved easily by writing the corresponding algebraic equations. These transformations are sufficient for the reduction of a cascade

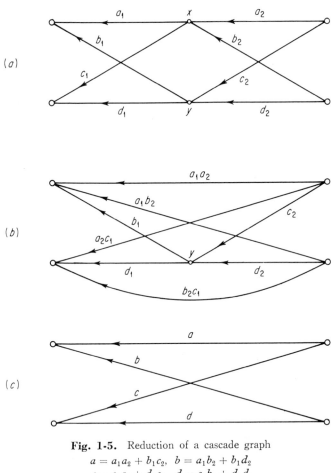

Fig. 1-5. Reduction of a cascade graph
$$a = a_1 a_2 + b_1 c_2, \quad b = a_1 b_2 + b_1 d_2$$
$$c = c_1 a_2 + d_1 c_2, \quad d = c_1 b_2 + d_1 d_2$$

graph. Thus, if the node x is removed in the graph of Fig. 1-5a, one obtains the graph shown in Fig. 1-5b from which the residual graph of Fig. 1-5c is obtained by absorption of the node y. Instead of operating in successive steps, one can eliminate several nodes by computing the residual transmittances in the original graph. The *residual transmittances* are the transmittances of the residual graph. If one shows the residual nodes in the original graph, for example by circles of larger diameter than for the other nodes (Fig. 1-5a), the residual transmittances can be evaluated in all the paths going from a residual node to another residual node without going through

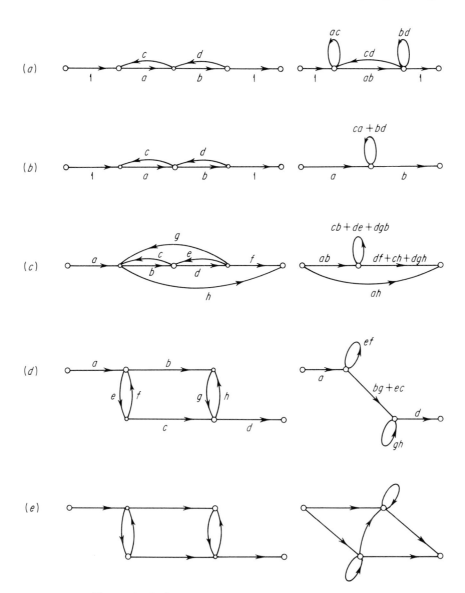

Fig. 1-6. Reduction by using elementary transformations

any other residual node. The residual graph of Fig. 1-5c, for example, can then be obtained directly from Fig. 1-5a.

Elementary transformations can be applied in feedback graphs in order to eliminate certain nodes; such transformations do not necessarily reduce the complexity of the graph. Thus, the transformation shown in Fig. 1-6a gives a residual graph with an index greater than that of the original graph. If sources, sinks, and index nodes are chosen as residual nodes, then the elementary transformations will give an index residual graph in which the index is the same as in the initial graph. Examples of such transformations are given in Fig. 1-6. Since, in general, the choice of index nodes is not unique, it is possible to obtain more than one index-residual graph from the same original graph as shown in Figs. 1-6d and e.

2) An index-residual graph containing only sources and sinks besides index nodes cannot be reduced further without the **elimination of a loop.** The elimination of a self-loop, shown in Fig. 1-7, is described by the solution of the equations:

$$x_1 = x_0 + gx_1 \qquad (1\text{-}6)$$
$$x_2 = x_1$$

in terms of the variable x_0:

$$x_2 = \frac{1}{1-g}x_0 \qquad (1\text{-}7)$$

If desired, one may retain an internal node in this transformation by dividing by one minus the loop transmittance, the transmittances of either the converging or the diverging branches as shown in Fig. 1-7b. It is to be noted that only the first of these transformations represents the same variable at the internal node.

The result of the elimination of a loop can also be interpreted as the sum of all the residual transmittances between the source and the sink of the graph in Fig. 1-7a. There are, in fact, an infinite number of residual paths passing through the loop zero, once, twice, ... n times respectively. The residual transmittance is then:

$$1 + g + g^2 + g^3 \dots \qquad (1\text{-}8)$$

This expression converges if $|g| < 1$. For values greater than one, it is possible to represent g by two branches of transmittances g_1 and g_2 such that $g_1 + g_2 = g$ and $|g_1| < 1$, and to eliminate the internal loop by the method shown in Fig. 1-7b. One then sums the residual transmittances as before:

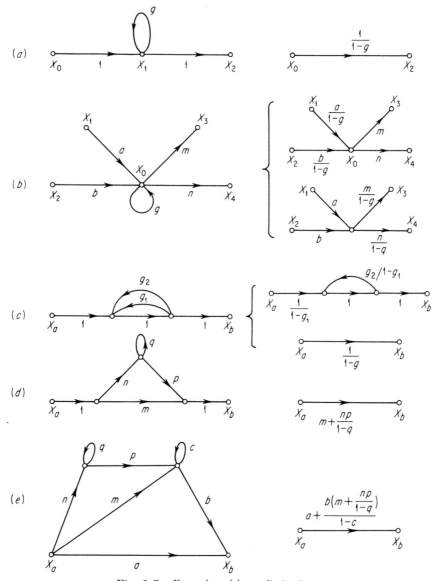

Fig. 1-7. Examples of loop elimination

$$\frac{1}{1-g_1} + \frac{g_2}{(1-g_1)^2} + \frac{g_2^2}{(1-g_1)^3} + \ldots = \frac{1}{1-g} \qquad (1\text{-}9)$$

This result converges if $|g_2/(1-g_1)| < 1$. The analytic continuation leads to the conclusion that the loop elimination by Eq. (1-7) holds for all values of g except 1.

Loop elimination and elementary transformations are sufficient for the complete reduction of any graph. In particular, if the graph has an index of one, or has only loop subgraphs of index one, the reduction of the graph is accomplished in one step as in Figs. 1-7d and 1-7e. For graphs of greater complexity, the index can be reduced by one at each step by absorption of one index node.

3) Examples of such a procedure are given in Fig. 1-8. In such cases, one can verify that the new transmittances can be written with the help of a **reduction formula**:

$$t'_{ij} = t_{ij} + \frac{t_{ik}t_{kj}}{1 - t_{kk}} \tag{1-10}$$

where indices i and j pertain to residual nodes and k to a node which disappears in the reduction. The residual transmittance between nodes i and j is the sum of all residual transmittances in the original

(a)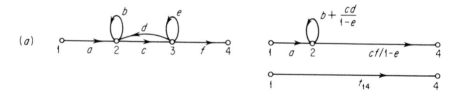

(b)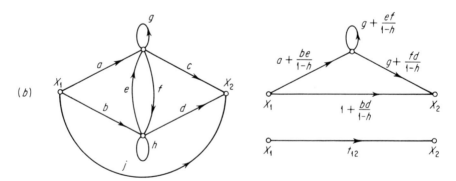

Fig. 1-8. Reduction of graphs with an index greater than one

$$t_{14} = \frac{\dfrac{acf}{1 - e}}{1 - b - \dfrac{cd}{1 - e}}$$

$$t_{12} = j + \frac{bd}{1 - h} + \frac{\left(a + \dfrac{be}{1 - h}\right)\left(c + \dfrac{fd}{1 - h}\right)}{1 - g - \dfrac{ef}{1 - h}}$$

graph, with those transmittances going through node k modified by one minus the loop transmittance.

Using the transformations described thus far, it is possible to derive techniques which are useful in certain cases. If a loop subgraph consists of a ring of branches, one has only to evaluate the transmittances of the open paths going through this ring and to divide them by one minus the loop transmittance. For the graph shown in Fig. 1-9a, it is possible to write directly:

$$\frac{x_2}{x_1} = \frac{ag + afh + bdg + bdfh + ch + cedg}{1 - def}$$

If the graph contains self-loops, one can first consider a modified graph without these loops and then add the proper denominators in the transmittances of the paths which cross a node with a self-loop. In the graph of Fig. 1-9b, for example, by neglecting the self-loops, the ratio x_2 / x_1 is:

$$j + \frac{ac + afd + bd + bec}{1 - ef}$$

Self-loops will add a denominator $(1 - g)$ in those transmittances of

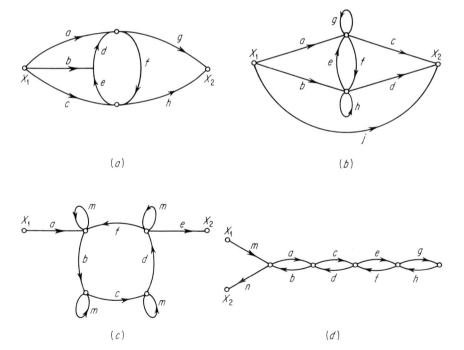

(a)

(b)

(c)

(d)

Fig. 1-9. Feedback graphs

the paths going through the upper node, and a denominator $(1 - h)$ in the path transmittances through the lower node. The transmission from source to sink for the complete graph is then:

$$\frac{x_2}{x_1} = j + \frac{\dfrac{ac}{1 - g} + \dfrac{afb + bec}{(1 - g)(1 - h)} + \dfrac{bd}{1 - h}}{1 - \dfrac{ef}{(1 - g)(1 - h)}}$$

The methods just described can be combined for the evaluation of the graph transmittance of Fig. 1-9c:

$$\frac{x_2}{x_1} = \frac{\dfrac{abcde}{(1 - m)^4}}{1 - \dfrac{bcdf}{(1 - m)^4}} \tag{1-11}$$

A chain of several loops as in the graph of Fig. 1-9d can be solved directly by considering the loops one after another:

$$\frac{x_2}{x_1} = \cfrac{mn}{1 - \cfrac{ab}{1 - \cfrac{cd}{1 - \cfrac{ef}{1 - gh}}}}$$

1-6 INVERSION

The inversion allows the reversal of the directions of certain branches in the graph. The topological properties of the graph are thus modified, and this is sometimes convenient either to facilitate the reduction or to establish certain relations. To invert a branch means to define the variable at the end of that branch with the help of an equation different from the one used in the original graph. One has then to isolate this variable on one side of the equation and to divide all the terms in the equation by the coefficient of that variable. This is illustrated in a simple case in Fig. 1-10a with the equations corresponding to the two graphs. A branch a can be inverted 1) by changing the direction on the branch and inverting its transmittance, 2) by moving the extremities of the branches which were converging with a so as to keep them converging in the new graph, and 3) by dividing the transmittances of these branches by the initial transmittance of a and changing their signs. The origins of these branches are not affected. The inversion of all the branches of a path constitutes the inversion of the path.

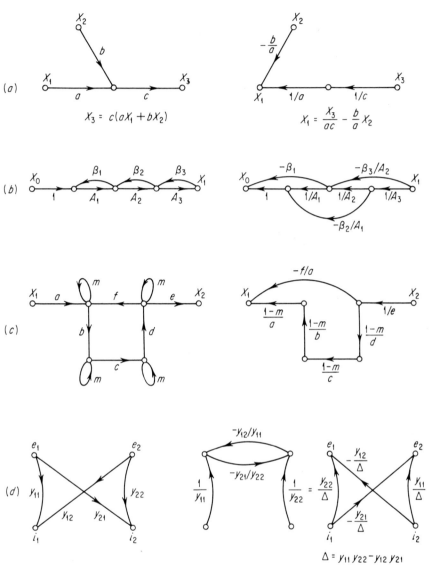

Fig. 1-10. Examples of inversion

Examples of inversions of paths from source to sink are given in Fig. 1-10b and c. In the first of these, the index is reduced from two to zero. The inversion will frequently produce a reduction of the index when the graph contains several loops and not too many paths parallel to the path which is inverted. If one desires to invert a path in which there are several branches, it is possibly easier to start the inversion at the source and to proceed towards the sink.

The transmittance of an inverted path is evidently the inverse of the transmittance of the original path. This transmittance will be easier to evaluate if the inversion reduces the index of the graph. The inversion, in the case of Fig. 1-10c in particular, leads to the expression:

$$\frac{1}{\frac{x_2}{x_1}} = \frac{1}{e}\left[\frac{-f}{a} + \frac{(1-m)^4}{abcd}\right] = \frac{1}{\frac{abcde}{(1-m)^4 - bcdf}} \tag{1-12}$$

and this result agrees with the value of Eq. (1-11) found in the original graph.

A last example of inversion is depicted in Fig. 1-10d which represents a graph for the admittance matrix of a two-terminal pair network. The inversion of the paths from source to sink produces the graph shown in the middle of the figure and this graph is transformed finally to a form corresponding to the impedance matrix of the network. The inversion of other paths in this graph would produce graphs for other matrices of the two-terminal pair network.

1-7 DIRECT SOLUTION: MASON'S RULE

It is not necessary to reduce the graph if the desired result is the overall transmission from source to sink, or from a source to some internal node. Mason's rule gives this result directly[10] with the help of the formula:

$$x_j = x_0 \frac{\sum_k G_k D_k}{D} \tag{1-13}$$

where x_0 is the source and x_j is the desired variable. If the graph contains several sources, one uses superposition.

In the denominator of this formula, D is the **determinant of the graph,** that is the determinant of the system of equations which the graph represents. This determinant is obtained directly from the graph by the expression:

$$D = 1 - \sum P_{m_1} + \sum P_{m_2} - \sum P_{m_3} + \dots \tag{1-14}$$

where: G_k is the transmittance of the k-th open path between the node x_0 and the node x_j,

       P_{mn} is the product of the transmittances of the m-th set of n nontouching loops. A nontouching or nonintersecting loop set is a set of loops not having any node in common.

D_k is the determinant of that part of the graph which does not touch the k-th open path: this determinant is called path factor of path k and can be evaluated by re-applying the Eq. (1-14) to a subgraph in which all the nodes of path k are split.

Fig. 1-11 is a detailed example of the application of this formula. In a, b, c, d, are shown all the loops of the graph. The sum of the loop transmittances give the term $\sum P_{m_1}$. Fig. 1-11e gives the only set of two nonintersecting loops which exists in this graph and the sum $\sum P_{m_2}$ has only one term, that is $adef$. There are no sets of three or more nonintersecting loops, and the evaluation of the determinant is completed by adding the terms already obtained. There are two open paths from the source to the node x_4 and these are shown in Figures f and g. The first of these paths touches all the loops, thus the path factor is one. The other open path has a transmittance equal to g and does not intersect the loop of transmittance be. The path transmittance is then multiplied by a path factor $(1 - be)$. The expression for the desired graph transmittance is shown in the top part of the figure.

In practice, it is not necessary to draw the several subgraphs shown in Fig. 1-11. It is sufficient to enumerate all the loops and to verify the nonintersection of these loops taking them one at a time, two at a time, and so on. This is easily achieved by considering the nodes of one part of the graph to be split; the loops which remain do not intersect the part considered.

The use of Mason's rule provides directly the output voltage e_{01} of the difference amplifier of Fig. 1-2c:

$$e_{01} = \frac{e_1 A_1 (1 + G_2 R_k / R_{L_2}) - e_2 A_2 G_1 R_k / R_{L_2}}{1 + G_1 R_k / R_{L_1} + G_2 R_k / R_{L_2}}$$

and the current in the last mesh of the network of Fig. 1-2b:

$$\frac{i_3}{e_1} = \frac{\dfrac{1}{Z_1} \dfrac{Z_2}{Z_3} \dfrac{Z_4}{(Z_5 + Z_6)}}{1 + \dfrac{Z_2}{Z_1} + \dfrac{Z_3}{Z_2} + \dfrac{Z_4}{Z_3} + \dfrac{Z_4}{Z_5 + Z_6} + \dfrac{Z_2}{Z_1}\left[\dfrac{Z_4}{Z_3} + \dfrac{Z_4}{Z_5 + Z_6}\right] + \dfrac{Z_2 Z_4}{Z_3(Z_5 + Z_6)}}$$

Mason's rule, already stated in part by Tustin[2] has been proved by Mason[10] himself, starting from the properties of flow graphs, and also analytically by Lorens[11]. Another demonstration[12] is sketched below.

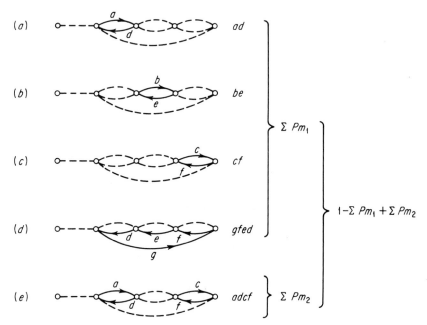

$$\frac{X_4}{X_0} = \frac{abc + g(1-be)}{1-ad-be-cf-gfed-adcf}$$

(a) ad

(b) be

(c) cf $\Sigma\, Pm_1$

(d) $gfed$ $1-\Sigma\, Pm_1 + \Sigma\, Pm_2$

(e) $adcf$ $\Big\}\ \Sigma\, Pm_2$

(f) $G_1 = abc$ $D_1 = 1$

(g) $G_2 = g$ $D_2 = 1-be$

Fig. 1-11. Application of Mason's rule

For the system of equations with matrix A:

$$A = \begin{bmatrix} a_{11} & a_{12} & a_{13} & \cdots & a_{1n} \\ a_{21} & a_{22} & & \cdots & a_{2n} \\ \cdots & \cdots & & & \\ \cdots & \cdots & & & \\ a_{n1} & a_{n2} & & \cdots & a_{nn} \end{bmatrix} \qquad (1\text{-}15)$$

it is possible to draw a flow graph whose transmittances are defined by Eq. (1-3). The matrix of the equations represented by the graph is then:

$$A = U - T = \begin{bmatrix} 1 - t_{11} & - t_{21} & \cdots & - t_{n1} \\ - t_{12} & 1 - t_{22} & \cdots & - t_{n2} \\ - t_{13} & - t_{23} & \cdots & - t_{n3} \\ \cdot & \cdot & & \cdot \\ \cdot & \cdot & & \cdot \\ \cdot & \cdot & & \cdot \\ - t_{1n} & - t_{2n} & \cdots & 1 - t_{nn} \end{bmatrix} \qquad (1\text{-}16)$$

In terms of the elements of the matrix A, the determinant of the system of equations is given by:

$$D = \sum (-1)^{I+I'} (a_{\alpha\alpha'}, a_{\beta\beta'}, a_{\gamma\gamma'}, \ldots, a_{nn'}) \qquad (1\text{-}17)$$

where each term contains n elements, one and only one taken from each row and each column, and where I and I' are the number of inversions of the numbers $1, 2, \ldots, n$, in the sequences of indices α, $\beta, \gamma, \ldots$ and $\alpha', \beta', \gamma', \ldots$. The sum in Eq. (1-17) must be made for all possible choices of the elements of the matrix.

It will be shown that the terms in this sum consist of all the possible products of transmittances of nonintersecting loops. Consider any term in Eq. (1-17). This term contains the element a_{ij}. It also contains necessarily another element of row j, and this element can only be a_{ji} or a_{jk}. If it is a_{ji} one can find next an element a_{kl}, since one must choose an element in rows and columns other than i and j. If it is an element a_{jk}, it is possible to find an element from row k which has to be a_{ki} or a_{kl}. Proceeding in this manner for each term in Eq. (1-17) and changing the order of the factors, one can write for the indices one or several closed sequences:

$$ij, jk, kl, lx, \ldots, yp, pi \qquad (1\text{-}18)$$

$$ij, ji, \ldots, nm, mp, pn, \ldots, qu, uq \qquad (1\text{-}19)$$

The number of inversions I' then becomes $I' = (I + n + K)$, n being the number of factors in each term and K the number of sequences.

Instead of the matrix A, the matrix corresponding to the flow graph in Eq. (1-16) will now be considered. By inverting the order in Eqs. (1-18) and (1-19), and by decomposing into several terms the terms containing elements of the first diagonal of the matrix, the following expressions are obtained:

$$t_{ip} t_{py} \cdots \qquad\qquad t_{xl} t_{lk} t_{kj} t_{ji} \qquad (1\text{-}20)$$

$$t_{qu} t_{uq} \cdots \quad (1) \cdots \quad t_{np} t_{pm} t_{mn} \cdots \quad t_{ij} t_{ji} \qquad (1\text{-}21)$$

$$t_{qu} t_{uq} \cdots \quad t_{rr} \cdots \quad t_{np} t_{pm} t_{mn} \cdots \quad t_{ij} t_{ji} \qquad (1\text{-}22)$$

The sign in front of each product is determined by taking into account the minus signs of the transmittances, hence:

$$(-1)^{l+l'+n} \tag{1-23}$$

which can be rewritten by substituting the value found previously for I':

$$(-1)^{l+l'+n+K+n} = (-1)^{2(1+n)+K} = (-1)^K \tag{1-24}$$

Each of the Eqs. (1-20, 21, 22) can be recognized as a loop transmittance or a product of loop transmittances, since the sequences in the indices start at a node and end at the same node. If one line contains several loops, the nonintersection is assured by the initial restriction on the choice of the elements of each term. The sign in front of each term depends uniquely on the number of loops as shown in Eq. (1-24). If one adds a term unity obtained from the product of the elements on the principal diagonal one can, by regrouping the terms, rewrite the determinant:

$$D = 1 - \sum P_{m_1} + \sum P_{m_2} - \sum P_{m_3} \cdots \tag{1-25}$$

The numerator of the expression for a variable such as x_2, for example, if there exists a nonzero left-hand number in the first equation only, is given by Cramer's rule as the determinant:

$$\begin{vmatrix} a_{11} & x_0 & a_{13} & \cdots & a_{1n} \\ a_{21} & 0 & a_{23} & \cdots & a_{2n} \\ \cdots & & & & \\ \cdots & & & & \\ a_{n1} & 0 & a_{n3} & \cdots & a_{nn} \end{vmatrix} \tag{1-26}$$

By writing the terms of the determinant in the same manner as before, one obtains closed sequences for the indices and one open sequence starting with 2 and ending with 1 which will be associated with the element x_0:

$$x_0 a_{2j} a_{jk} a_{kl} \cdots a_{rr} \cdots a_{pq} a_{qs} a_{sp} \tag{1-27}$$

Using the matrix of the flow graph in Eq. (1-16) and writing the factors corresponding to the preceding indices, starting from the right, one gets:

$$x_0 t_{lk} t_{kj} t_{j2} \cdots t_{rr} \cdots t_{ps} t_{sq} t_{qp} \tag{1-28}$$

$$x_0 t_{lk} t_{kj} t_{j2} \cdots (1) \cdots t_{ps} t_{sq} t_{qp} \tag{1-29}$$

In all the terms obtained, there will be a path transmittance for a path from node 1 to node 2, and each of these transmittances will be multiplied by a product of loop transmittances. These loops cannot intersect the path considered because of the initial restriction on the choice of the elements in the Eq. (1–17) of the determinant. Combining all these results one can then finally write:

$$x_2 = x_0 \sum \frac{G_k D_k}{D} \qquad (1\text{–}30)$$

2

Signal Flow Graphs
and Feedback Theory

2-1 INTRODUCTION

In the first chapter, the analogy between the loop in the flow graph and the concept of feedback was noted. Generalizing the definition of loop transmittance, Mason[10] has defined the loop transmittance for a branch or for a node and also the return difference for a branch or for a node. This last definition is precisely the mathematical definition of feedback as introduced by Bode. It thus becomes evident that on the one hand the theory of flow graphs has been greatly influenced by Bode and on the other hand, flow graphs permit a very elegant presentation of the mathematical properties of feedback. In reviewing these properties briefly in this chapter, we shall try to stress the relations between flow graphs and feedback theory.

In the first sentences of his Chapt. 4, Bode[8] first describes a feedback amplifier as a network composed of an ordinary amplifier of gain μ and of a return or feedback circuit of gain β. The feedback is then determined from the product $\mu\beta$, representing the gain of the loop formed by the circuits μ and β together. This network possesses the important property that the variations in the μ circuit produced by a deviation of linearity or by noise are reduced by the factor $1 - \mu\beta$, from the values they would have without feedback. From the first definition, Bode then goes to a mathematical definition of feedback to which all his Chapt. 4 is devoted. This mathematical definition, in terms of the loop or node equations of the network, is the ratio of two determinants:

$$F = \frac{\Delta}{\Delta_0} \qquad (2\text{-}1)$$

which becomes, with flow graphs, the return difference of a branch or of a node. The letter F will be used for feedback instead of the D used by Bode because D has already been used for the determinant of the graph.

This mathematical definition is a purely mathematical concept as is the loop of a flow graph. Such a definition permits the derivation of certain mathematical properties but it is completely devoid of physical meaning. This is easily realized when one applies the Eq. (2-1) to a set of linear algebraic equations. The feedback for a coefficient k of a variable x in such a system of equations is defined as one minus the value obtained for x when the independent variables are made zero and kx is made equal to one. If the equations represent the equilibrium of an electrical network, the feedback is one minus k times the value obtained for some current or voltage variable x, when a unit source is applied for kx and all other sources are removed. The coefficient k in this case is an impedance or an admittance or a dimensionless coefficient according to whether the unit source has the same dimensions as the observed variable x or not. However, the current or the voltage is not necessarily a current or a voltage really existing in the network; it can be a combination of the currents of several branches or it can be the voltage of the incident wave in the theory of the quadripole. Similarly, the impedance is not necessarily a physical element of the network; it can be some transfer function, for example. The purely physical properties of feedback, such as the opening of a loop and the measurement of the returned quantity, or the reduction of undesired effects by a factor F, are not included in the Eq. (2-1). It is only when the equations of the physical system are written in a certain way, and when k represents a physical element of the network, that the mathematical definition corresponds to those physical properties which constituted the initial definition of feedback. This is evident even in Bode, for example when he computes feedback for a reference other than zero. Other examples will be given later in this chapter.

There is feedback in the sense of the Eq. (2-1) when the mind perceives a closed chain of relations around a given variable. In some problems, the structure of the problem itself shows explicitly such a chain of relations: feedback amplifiers or servo loops are good examples. In a system of equations, such a chain of relations may not appear as explicitly. With flow graphs however, such chains of relations correspond to loops in the graph and are plainly evident. This study will be restricted to the mathematical definition of feedback, and to the properties which derive from this definition.

In order to visualize Eq. (2-1) in the flow graph, it is necessary first to generalize the idea of loop. Some properties which derive from this definition will then be proved, and the relations with known theorems of Bode will be indicated. Several of these properties have been illustrated by Mason[10] himself with signal flow graphs, others by Truxal[13] in his book on servomechanisms.

2-2   LOOP TRANSMITTANCE AND RETURN DIFFERENCE

2-2-1. Generalization of the idea of loop. The idea of loop introduced in the first chapter must be extended before it can be applied to feedback problems. This generalization introduces as new concepts the **loop transmittance of a node** and the **loop transmittance of a branch**. The loop transmittance of a node is defined as the transmittance of the path from the source half node to the sink half node created by splitting the node for which the loop transmittance is desired. In terms of the signal analogy, it is the signal returned to a node when a unit signal is applied at that node. The examples a and b of Fig. 2-1 give the loop transmittances of the nodes indicated. The **return difference of a node** k is one minus the loop transmittance T_k of the node:

$$F_k = 1 - T_k \qquad (2-2)$$

The symbol F will be used for return difference. An example is given in Fig. 2-1c.

The loop transmittance of a branch is defined as the loop transmittance of an extra node added in this branch. One can always add

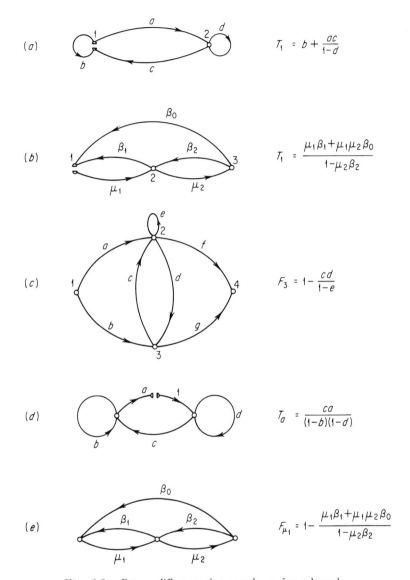

$$(a) \qquad T_1 = b + \frac{ac}{1-d}$$

$$(b) \qquad T_1 = \frac{\mu_1\beta_1 + \mu_1\mu_2\beta_0}{1-\mu_2\beta_2}$$

$$(c) \qquad F_3 = 1 - \frac{cd}{1-e}$$

$$(d) \qquad T_a = \frac{ca}{(1-b)(1-d)}$$

$$(e) \qquad F_{\mu_1} = 1 - \frac{\mu_1\beta_1 + \mu_1\mu_2\beta_0}{1-\mu_2\beta_2}$$

Fig. 2-1. Return difference for a node or for a branch

an extra node by replacing a given branch by the combination of two cascade branches, one of which has a unit transmittance. In Fig. 2–1d, the loop transmittance is evaluated for the branch of transmittance a. The **return difference of a branch** is also defined by Eq. (2-2) using as T_k the loop transmittance of the branch, as illustrated in Fig. 2–1e.

2-2-2. *Properties.* Because all the transformations of graphs use only linear algebra, the transmittances calculated in a graph are linear rational functions of the transmittance of any branch one wishes to consider explicitly. If g is such a transmittance, any more general transmittance evaluated from the graph will be of the form:

$$G = \frac{a + bg}{c + dg} \qquad (2\text{-}3)$$

where the constants a, b, c, d, are functions of the other branches. In the particular case where the branch g is directly attached to the source or to the sink of the path for which the transmittance is evaluated, one has a linear relation:

$$G = m + ng \qquad (2\text{-}4)$$

Because the loop transmittances of a branch or of a node and the return differences have the character of transmittances, F_k is also a rational function of any branch of the graph, and a linear function of any branch directly attached to the node k or in cascade with the branch k. One notes that only the branches of the feedback unit which contains the branch of interest will appear in the expression of the return difference: branches attached to a source or to a sink need not be considered in the evaluation of return differences.

2-2-3. *Partial return differences.* One can define a partial return difference for a node m as the return difference computed as above, in a graph where the nodes are numbered, by splitting the nodes of order greater than m. Thus, in the graph of Fig. 2-1b, the partial differences for the nodes 1, 2, 3 are:

$$D'_1 = 1$$
$$D'_2 = 1 - \mu_1\beta_1 \qquad (2\text{-}5)$$
$$D'_3 = 1 - \frac{\mu_2(\beta_2 + \beta_0)}{1 - \mu_1\beta_1}$$

If in a given graph, one removes all the nodes of order greater than m and the branches attached to these nodes, and then reduces the resulting graph to a residual graph containing only the two nodes $(m - 1)$ and m, one obtains the graph of Fig. 2-2 which give the partial return differences:

$$D'_{m-1} = 1 - b \qquad (2\text{-}6)$$

$$D'_m = 1 - e - \frac{cd}{1 - b} \qquad (2\text{-}7)$$

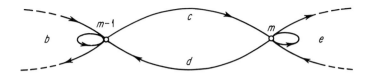

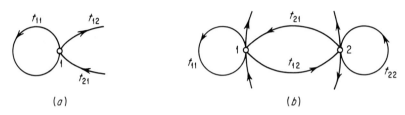

Fig. 2-2. Residual graph with nodes m and $m-1$

By changing the order of the nodes by a permutation of the orders for these two nodes, the new partial return differences are:

$$D''_{m-1} = 1 - e \tag{2-8}$$

$$D''_m = 1 - b - \frac{cd}{1-e} \tag{2-9}$$

It is easy to verify that the product of the two partial return differences is constant, independently of the order of numbering of the nodes m and $(m-1)$. Proceeding in this way from node to node in the graph, it can be shown that the product of the partial return differences for all the nodes of the graph is a constant independent of the order in which the nodes are taken. This invariant is the determinant of the graph:

$$D = D'_1 D'_2 D'_3 \dots D'_n \tag{2-10}$$

This statement can be proved by using a general graph with transmittances t_{jk} between nodes j and k, and self-loops of transmittances t_{jj}. The determinant of the graph is the determinant of the matrix introduced in the first chapter:

$$D = |U - T| = \begin{vmatrix} 1 - t_{11} & -t_{21} & -t_{31} & \cdot & \cdot \\ -t_{12} & 1 - t_{22} & & \cdot & \cdot \\ -t_{13} & \cdot & & \cdot & \cdot \\ & \cdot & \cdot & & \cdot \\ & \cdot & & & \end{vmatrix} \tag{2-11a}$$

which can be reduced to triangular form:

$$
D = \begin{vmatrix}
(1 - t_{11}) & -t_{21} & -t_{31} & \cdot & \cdot \\
0 & \left(1 - t_{22} - \dfrac{t_{12}t_{21}}{1 - t_{11}}\right) & -t_{32} - \dfrac{t_{31}t_{12}}{1 - t_{11}} & \cdot & \\
0 & 0 & 0 & \cdot & \\
0 & 0 & 0 & & \\
\cdot & \cdot & \cdot & &
\end{vmatrix}
\qquad (2\text{-}11b)
$$

If the partial return difference is computed in this graph for the first node, all the other nodes being split (Fig. 2–3a), the following result is obtained:

$$ D_1' = 1 - t_{11} \qquad (2\text{-}12) $$

For the partial return difference of the second node, the residual Graph in Fig. 2–3b is used and gives:

$$ D_2' = 1 - t_{22} - \frac{t_{12}t_{21}}{1 - t_{11}} \qquad (2\text{-}13) $$

The partial return difference of node 3 can be evaluated in the last graph of Fig. 2–3:

$$ D_3' = 1 - t_{33} - \frac{t_{13}t_{31}}{1 - t_{11}} - \frac{\left(t_{23} - \dfrac{t_{21}t_{13}}{1 - t_{11}}\right)\left(t_{32} - \dfrac{t_{31}t_{12}}{1 - t_{11}}\right)}{1 - t_{22} - \dfrac{t_{12}t_{21}}{1 - t_{11}}} \qquad (2\text{-}14) $$

One can continue in this fashion and verify that the partial return differences obtained are the elements of the diagonal of the triangular

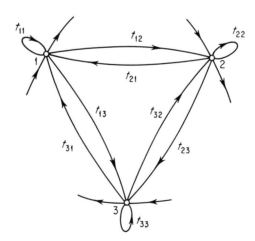

Fig. 2-3. Residual graphs for the evaluation of partial return differences

matrix in Fig. (2-11b). Hence, the Eq. (2-10) for the determinant is proved.

2-2-4. Return difference of a branch or of a node. Since $D_n' = F_n$ for the node numbered last, the return difference for the node n is readily obtained from Eqs. (2-10) and (2-2):

$$D_n' = 1 - T_n = F_n = \frac{D}{D_1' D_2' \cdots D_{n-1}'}$$

Since the order in which the nodes are taken does not change this result, any node k can be numbered the last, and the return difference for any node k can then be written:

$$F_k = \frac{D}{D_k} \qquad (2\text{-}15)$$

In this expression, D is the determinant of the graph, and D_k is the determinant computed with the node k split. The return difference for any branch jk becomes:

$$F_{jk} = \frac{D}{D_{jk}} \qquad (2\text{-}16)$$

where D_{jk} is the determinant computed in the graph with the branch jk removed (or with an extra node introduced in this branch and split).

2-3 FEEDBACK

2-3-1. Definition of feedback. It should now be evident that the definition of return difference for a branch of the graph is precisely the mathematical definition of feedback, according to Bode's definition:

"The return difference, or feedback, for any element in a complete circuit is equal to the ratio of the values assumed by the circuit determinant when the specified element has its normal value and when the specified element vanishes."

To compute the feedback for an element, it is sufficient to have the element represented by only one branch of the flow graph and to evaluate the return difference for that branch. The condition that the element appears only once in the graph is equivalent to the condition imposed by Bode that the equilibrium equations be written in such a way that the element for which feedback is computed is in a definite position of the matrix. This element must be a constituent of a diagonal term of the matrix if it is a bilateral element, and it must appear in a term ij ($i \neq j$) if it is a unilateral element. In

this way, the element for which feedback is computed will appear
only once in the system of equations; the same restriction holds with
flow graphs.   It is to be noted that Bode defines the loop transmission as the negative of what we have defined as the loop transmittance of a branch.   Hence, feedback in Bode is expressed with a plus
sign in the equation equivalent to our Eq. (2-2).

Two examples taken from Bode are illustrated in Fig. 2-4 with
flow graphs.   The return difference is computed for a bilateral element.   In Fig. 2-4a, the feedback is computed for the element Z.   In
the graph, the transmittance Z defines the output voltage produced by
the current i, and the current is obtained as the difference of the
currents in the other two impedances.   The feedback for the element
Z is then:

$$F_Z = 1 - Z\left(\frac{-1}{Z_1} + \frac{-1}{Z_2}\right) \qquad (2\text{-}17)$$

In the example of Fig. 2-4b, all the resistances are equal to 1 ohm,
and feedback for the element Z is required.   The graph is obtained
using superposition.   Short-circuiting Z, the source e will produce a
contribution to the current i, and the transmittance of the branch
corresponding to this relation is not shown explicitly since it is not
required in the computation (this branch being attached to a source
node).   One considers next a source e_z while the source e is short-

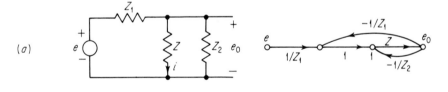

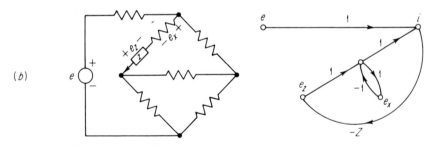

Fig. 2-4.   Return difference for a bilateral element

circuited. The difference $e_z - e_x$ is the voltage across a new balanced bridge with all the branches of the bridge being 1 ohm. This difference divided by 1 ohm will give the other contribution to the current i. It remains only, to complete the graph, to define the variables e_x and e_z from the known currents. The return difference for the element Z is then:

$$F_z = 1 + \frac{Z}{2} \tag{2-18}$$

The Eqs. (2-15) and (2-16) are more general than the restricted use feedback analysts make of them when they compute feedback for a physical element, such as the transconductance g_m of a vacuum tube. The concept of feedback, as defined mathematically in Eq. (2-15), is applicable to any problem in which one perceives a closed chain of relations between the variables. This becomes evident in flow graphs which contain, generally, several loops, and is illustrated in the example of Fig. 2-5. The two-terminal pair network of Fig. 2-5a is specified by its driving-point and transfer impedances and one possible graph is shown in Fig. 2-5b. From this graph, the return difference for the element Z_{21} can be computed as:

$$F_{Z_{21}} = 1 - \frac{\dfrac{Z_{21}Z_{12}}{Z_{11}Z_L}}{1 + \dfrac{Z_{22}}{Z_L}}$$

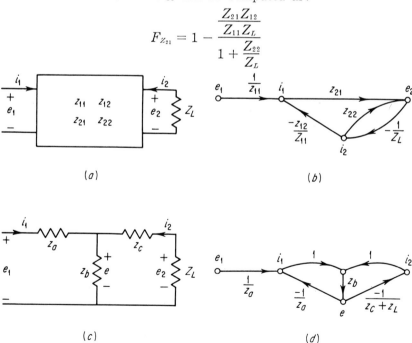

(a)   (b)

(c)   (d)

Fig. 2-5. Examples of return differences

However, if the feedback is computed for the element z_b in the two-port network of Fig. 2-5c with the help of the graph of Fig. 2-5d, the following result is obtained:

$$F_{Z_b} = 1 + z_b \left(\frac{1}{z_a} + \frac{1}{z_c + z_L} \right)$$

and evidently $F_{Z_{21}} \neq F_{z_b}$ although the first quadripole represents the T circuit if one makes $z_b = Z_{21}$. The feedback F_{z_b} involves the loop transmittance (z_b / z), which is the ratio of the impedance z_b to the impedance z presented by the network across the same points according to Bode (feedback for a reciprocal element) and according to the flow graph. The feedback $F_{Z_{21}}$ satisfies the mathematical definition of feedback but does not possess the physical properties included in the feedback for a physical element.

2-3-2. Feedback for a reference other than zero. The feedback computed with a reference other than zero is a concept useful to Bode, but much less needed in flow graph analysis. One can, how ever, interpret this concept in terms of flow graphs. If it is desired to find the feedback for an element W for a reference different from zero, the branch W is decomposed into two parallel branches of transmittances W_0 and W' such that $W_0 + W' = W$, and the feedback is evaluated for the branch W'. A residual graph for the branch W is shown in Fig. 2-6a, and the feedback for W becomes:

$$F_W = 1 - WT$$

The feedback for the branch W' in Fig. 2-6b gives:

$$F_{W'} = 1 - \frac{W'T}{1 - W_0 T} = \frac{1 - WT}{1 - W_0 T}$$

and with the help of the preceeding equation, one can write:

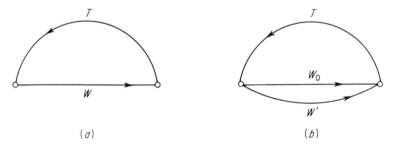

(a) (b)

Fig. 2-6. Residual graph for the definition of feedback with a reference other than zero

$$F_{W'} = \frac{F_W}{F_{W(W=W_0)}} \qquad (2\text{-}19)$$

This result leads to Bode's theorem:

"The return difference of W for any reference is equal to the ratio of the return differences, with zero reference, which would be obtained if W assumed, first, its nominal value, and second the chosen reference value."

2-3-3. *Generalization of loop elimination.* The concept of return difference for a node allows a generalization of the elimination of a loop described in the first chapter. It is easily verified that the trans-

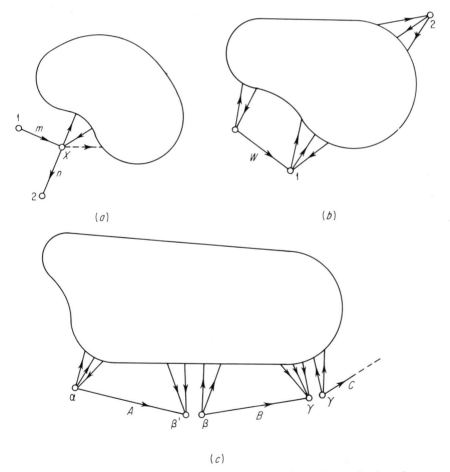

(a)   (b)

(c)

Fig. 2-7. Applications of the return difference of a node or of a branch (in these graphs only the branches and nodes of interest are shown explicitly)

mission at a node (Mason's "injection gain of a node") contained in a direct path as node x in Fig. 2–7a, is modified by the feedback at that node. It is then possible to write for the transmittance from source to sink:

$$T_{12} = \frac{mn}{F_x} \qquad (2\text{-}20)$$

where F_x is the return difference for node x.

The feedback for an element is used by Bode in three theorems which he includes under a common title "*Thevenin's theorem in active circuits.*" The fundamental idea of these theorems is illustrated in Fig. 2–7b which allows one to express the transmission between two given nodes of the graph in terms of the transmittance of a branch attached to one of these two nodes:

$$T_{12} = \frac{T_{12(W=0)}}{F_W} \qquad (2\text{-}21)$$

In this expression, F_W is the feedback for the branch W. This result can be proved by drawing a residual graph and using Eq. (2–20).

Eq. (2–20) can also be used to evaluate the transmission between any two nodes of an open path by obtaining one after the other the transmissions between successive nodes. In the open path A–B–C of Fig. 2–7c for example, after having split all the nodes of this open path except the first, one obtains for the graph transmittance between the nodes α and β' (assuming that no other open path exists):

$$T_{\alpha\beta'} = \frac{A}{D'_\alpha} \qquad (2\text{-}22)$$

The partial return difference D'_α requires that all the nodes of the open path are split except the first one. The transmission from the second node (unsplit) to the third is:

$$T_{\beta\gamma'} = \frac{B}{D'_\beta} \qquad (2\text{-}23)$$

The partial difference D'_β requires that all the nodes of the open path, except the first two are split. Proceeding this way for the complete open path between a node x_0 and a node x_j, one obtains the graph transmittance:

$$\frac{ABC\ldots}{D'_\alpha D'_\beta D'_\gamma \ldots} \qquad (2\text{-}24)$$

If there are several parallel open paths between the two nodes, it is necessary to sum all the transmissions and the final result takes the form:

$$\frac{x_j}{x_0} = \sum_i \frac{G_i}{D'_{\alpha_i} D'_{\beta_i} D'_{\gamma_i} \cdots} \qquad (2\text{-}25)$$

G_i is the transmittance of one open path, and $D'_{\alpha_i} D'_{\beta_i} D'_{\gamma_i} \cdots$ is the product of the partial return differences for this open path. These partial return differences are evaluated by splitting all the nodes of the open path and closing them anew one by one.

The reduction to a common denominator of all the terms of the Eq. (2-25) will show that this result is just another statement of Mason's rule. The reader will probably recognize in that equation the gain formula for a multistage amplifier which can be written by first putting all the μ equal to zero, and then bringing μ back to its normal value in each stage in succession. In the numerator, $ABC...$ is the product of the gains of successive stages, and in the denominator appears the product of the return differences for each stage. The return difference for stage k is computed with a normal value of μ in the first k stages and a μ of zero for the following stages.

2-3-4. Feedback for two elements. Given any two branches of the graph, the return differences for these branches can be obtained

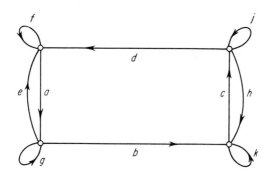

Fig. 2-8. Residual graph for the evaluation of the return difference for two elements

from the residual graph of Fig. 2-8. Taking for example the branches a and c, one gets the return differences:

$$F_a = 1 - \frac{a}{(1-g)(1-f)}\left[e + \frac{bcd}{(1-j)(1-k)-ch}\right] \qquad (2\text{-}26)$$

$$F_c = 1 - \frac{c}{(1-j)(1-k)}\left[h + \frac{bad}{(1-f)(1-g)-ae}\right] \qquad (2\text{-}27)$$

The return difference for each branch, computed when the other branch is open, is obtained from the preceeding equations or from the graph as:

$$F_{a(c=0)} = 1 - \frac{ae}{(1-g)(1-f)} \tag{2-28}$$

$$F_{c(a=0)} = 1 - \frac{ch}{(1-j)(1-k)} \tag{2-29}$$

The ratios of the return differences are seen to be the same in each case; taking into account the result in Eq. (2-19), we then have Bode's theorem:

"*The ratio between the actual return differences for any two elements, for any reference condition, is the same as the ratio which would be obtained if the return difference for each element were computed with the other element at its reference value.*"

2-4 SENSITIVITY

The sensitivity of the gain G to the variations of an element W of a system is generally defined as follows:

$$S = \frac{\dfrac{G}{W}}{\dfrac{dG}{dW}} \tag{2-30}$$

The gain is the graph transmittance between two variables of the system which can be taken as the source and the sink of a graph. A suitable graph is that of Fig. 2-9 which shows besides the source

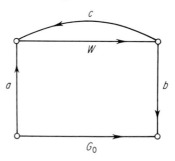

Fig. 2-9. Flow graph for the computation of sensitivity

and the sink the branch of transmittance W with respect to which the sensitivity will be computed. The transmittance from source to sink is evaluated as:

$$G = G_0 + \frac{abW}{1 - Wc} = G_0 + \frac{T_d}{F_W} \tag{2-31}$$

and the sensitivity becomes:

$$S = \frac{F_w}{1 - \frac{G_0}{G}} \quad (2\text{-}32)$$

if one defines:

T_d: The transmittance of the open path passing through the branch W: it is the gain without feedback and neglecting any direct transmission.

G_0: The direct transmission, or transmittance of the open path not going through W.

F_w: The feedback for the branch specified.

In a problem without direct transmission, Eq. (2-32) is equivalent to Bode's theorem:

"*The sensitivity and return difference are equal for any element whose vanishing leads to zero transmission through the circuit as a whole.*"

For example, the sensitivities for the elements Z in the networks of Fig. 2-4 will be the values already obtained in Eqs. (2-17) (2-18) for the return differences F_z.

In the case of a nonzero direct transmission, from Eq. (2-32) follows the theorem:

"*The sensitivity of the difference between the normal output and the direct transmission for any element W is equal to the return difference for W.*"

In order to facilitate the computation of sensitivities, Bode introduces the use of a reference other than zero for the feedback. This reference is the value which should be given to the specified element in order that the total transmission be zero. Let W_0 be that reference. If the branch W is replaced in the graph in Fig. 2-9 by two parallel branches, as it was done previously (Fig. 2-6b), the graph of Fig. 2-10 is obtained. The sensitivity for the branch W' will be the relative sensitivity S':

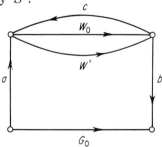

Fig. 2-10. Computation of the relative sensitivity

$$S' = F_{\text{II}''} \tag{2-33}$$

This relative sensitivity is equal to the return difference, because this graph has no direct transmission with the value chosen for W_0. Recalling the Eq. (2-30), the sensitivity S will be given by the relation:

$$\frac{S}{S'} = \frac{W'}{W} \tag{2-34}$$

The reference value W_0 can be obtained from the graph in Fig. 2-10 after removal of the branch W'. The graph transmittance from source to sink should be zero in this graph; it then follows that:

$$T = G_0 + \frac{ab W_0}{1 - W_0 c} = 0 \tag{2-35}$$

and the value of W_0 is the value given by Bode:

$$W_0 = \frac{G_0}{ab - cG_0} \tag{2-36}$$

With signal flow graphs, it is generally more convenient to reduce the graph to a residual form than to use a reference other than zero. Thus, in the example of Fig. 2-11a, a residual graph (Fig. 2-11b) is used to evaluate the sensitivity of the gain to the variations of the

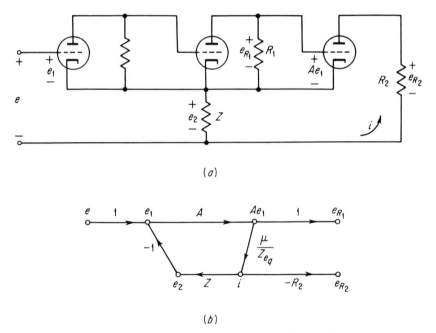

(a)

(b)

Fig. 2-11. Example of computation of sensitivity

μ of the last tube. In this graph, A represents the gain without feedback of the first two stages and Z_{eq} the impedance of the loop formed by the resistance of the last tube, R_2, and the impedance Z. If the output voltage is taken across R_2, there is no direct transmission and the sensitivity of the gain to the variations of the μ of the last stage is simply the return difference:

$$S_2 = 1 + \frac{\mu AZ}{Z_{eq}} \qquad (2\text{-}37\text{a})$$

If the output voltage is taken across R_1, there exists a transmission from input to output even if the μ of the last tube is made zero. Eq. (2-32) is then applied to obtain the sensitivity:

$$S_1 = \frac{1 + \mu AZ / Z_{eq}}{\mu AZ / Z_{eq}} \qquad (2\text{-}37\text{b})$$

2-5 IMPEDANCES

The impedance of a network can be written from a residual graph. which contains besides source and sink nodes, the branch for which the feedback is of interest. The source and the sink nodes represent the voltage and the current which will define the impedance specified. Such a graph is shown in Fig. 2-12a. Reducing this graph, one can write:

$$Z_{(W)} = Z_0 \frac{1}{1 - \dfrac{bcW}{1 - aW}} = Z_0 \frac{1 - aW}{1 - W(a + bc)} \qquad (2\text{-}38)$$

or the more general formula:

$$Z_{(W)} = Z_0 \frac{F_{W(0)}}{F_{W(\infty)}} \qquad (2\text{-}39)$$

if one notes:

Z_0: The impedance without feedback

$F_{W(0)}$: The return difference computed by short circuiting the nodes of the network across which the impedance is required. The node E in the graph of Fig. 2-12a will then be split.

$F_{W(\infty)}$: The feedback computed when these same nodes are open in the network, with the element W removed.

If the branch W has a value W_0, the same computation gives:

$$Z_{(W_0)} = Z_0 \frac{1 - aW_0}{1 - W_0(a + bc)} \qquad (2\text{-}40)$$

and the ratio of the values of the impedance Z (Eqs. 2-38 and 2-40) obtained in the two cases suggests another theorem of Bode (re-

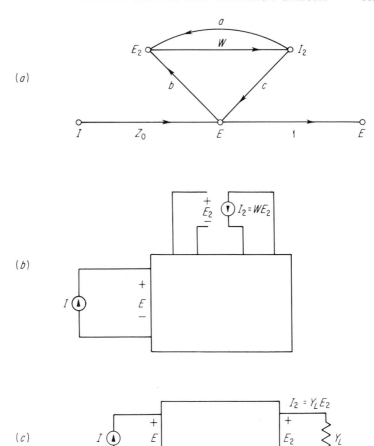

Fig. 2-12. Graph used in the derivation of the impedance formula of active or passive networks

membering the Eq. 2-19):

"*The ratio of the impedances seen at any point of a network when a given element W is assigned two different values is equal to the ratio of the return differences for W when the terminals between which the impedance is measured are first short-circuited and then open-circuited, if the return differences are computed by letting the first value of W be the operating value and the second the reference.*"

The concept of loop in the signal flow graph will show the identity between the properties derived from the mathematical definition of feedback and some theorems of network theory. Consider as an example the graph of Fig. 2–12a. On the one hand, this graph is a representation of the feedback circuit of Fig. 2–12b if the transmittance W is taken as the g_m of the tube. On the other hand, the same graph serves equally well as a representation of the passive network of Fig. 2–12c if the transmittance W is made equal to the load admittance Y_L. The effect of the load on the input impedance of the passive network is then given by the preceding theorem if the return difference of the element Y_L is used.

With the help of flow graphs, it is possible to compute the impedance directly from the graph if it contains a source node and a sink node representing the voltage and the current necessary to de-

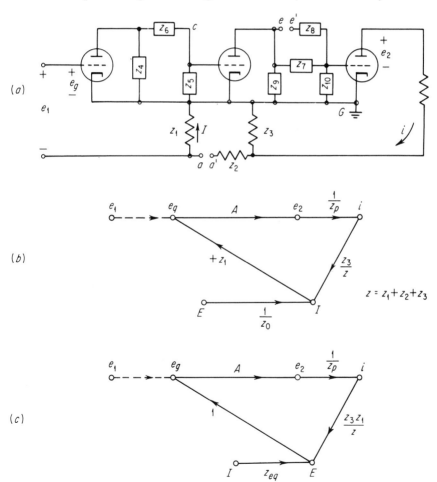

Fig. 2-13. Example for the impedance of an active network

fine this impedance. The return difference can also be computed by applying Eq. (2–39). Examples of both methods are given.

In the network of Fig. 2–13a, the impedance at the terminals a-a' can be measured by introducing a source e_{in} across these terminals and measuring the current I. The graph corresponding to this case is drawn in Fig. 2–13b, in which A is the gain without feedback and Z_p is the impedance of the plate circuit of the last stage. The impedance seen across a-a' is the transmission between the nodes E and I of the graph:

$$\frac{E}{I} \equiv Z_{aa'} = Z_0\left(1 - \frac{Z_1 A Z_3}{Z_p Z}\right)$$

The impedance between the point a and ground can be obtained from the graph of Fig. 2–13c where I now represents a current source applied in the network between the point a and ground. The graph transmittance from I to E will be the desired impedance. One can also use the graph of Fig. 2–13b and apply Eq. (2–39). Computing the return differences for Z_1, one obtains:

$$F_{(0)} = 1$$

$$F_{(\infty)} = \left(1 - \frac{Z_1 A Z_3}{Z_p Z}\right)$$

$$Z_0 = Z_{eq}$$

$$Z_{ag} = Z_0 \frac{1}{(1 - Z_1 A Z_3 / Z_p Z)}$$

The same equation yields the impedance across the points e-e' of the network after evaluation of the return differences, with the transmittance A taking different values according to the conditions at the terminals e-e' (short-circuit or open-circuit).

$$F_{(0)} = 1 - Z_1 A Z_3 / Z_p Z$$

$$F_{(\infty)} = 1 - Z_1 A' Z_3 / Z_p Z$$

$$Z_{(0)} = Z_8 + \frac{Z_7(Z_9 + Z_{10})}{Z_7 + Z_9 + Z_{10}}$$

$$Z_{ee'} = Z_{(0)} \frac{F_{(0)}}{F_{(\infty)}}$$

The gain A and its value A' when the impedance Z_8 is removed (the terminals e-e' being open-circuited) can be computed in a separate subgraph.

2-6 STABILITY

The study of stability in feedback systems makes use of the Nyquist criterion and this theory is well known, so that it is sufficient to mention only briefly the effect of several loops. It is convenient here to use an index-residual graph in which the nodes other than source and sink are numbered from 1 to n. The partial return differences D_k' are then computed (splitting the nodes of order higher than k). These return differences will be, in general, functions of the complex variable $p = \sigma + j\omega$, and Nyquist diagrams will be used to determine for each function the excess in the number of zeros over the number of poles. The gain of the system has a numerator formed from the (stable) transmittances of the graph and the denominator is the product of the partial return differences.

If the graph is reduced further than an index-residual graph, it is necessary to verify also that the transmittances in the graph are stable.

2-7 CONCLUSION

This brief study of feedback through signal flow graphs does not add much to the classical theory of Bode. The only interest of such a study resides in the simple and elegant method of presentation of classical results. Residual graphs permit an immediate perception of certain relationships, and constitute a graphical language which is facile and descriptive as compared to the equations of Bode with determinants and minors. In a given problem, the reduction of the initial graph will introduce naturally the residual graphs; thus, the use of Bode's theorems is somewhat superfluous. Moreover, signal flow graphs help the analyst to recognize the presence of feedback and to utilize its classical properties in many problems, whereas in other formulations it may remain undetected.

3

Direct Analysis of Electrical Networks Through Signal Flow Graphs

3-1 INTRODUCTION

Network theory is based in part on topology and algebra. For a given network, certain properties derive from the nature of the elements, but others result from the manner in which the elements are interconnected, independently of their nature. The incidence matrix completely describes the interconnection of the elements, and there exists a one-to-one correspondence between this matrix and the topology of the network. Other connection matrices, such as cut-set

Chapts. 3, 4, 5, 7 and the Appendix constitute the material of a Doctoral Dissertation to be submitted to the School of Graduate Studies of Laval University.

and tie-set matrices can be used to describe the geometry of the network and together with the element matrix, make it possible to write
the equilibrium equations. This method was described by Bayard[14]
and Foster[15], and the mathematical basis was established by Synge[16]
and Roth[17]. Parameter matrices (for example the admittance or
impedance matrices), and more recently, signal flow graphs[18, 19] have
been used to formulate the equilibrium equations of electrical networks.

In the direct method of analysis, flow graphs are used in a
particular form to represent Kirchhoff's equations of the network.
However, the resultant graph is not only a new formulation of the
equations. With the particular form chosen for these graphs, their
topology is either identical to that of the network or is the dual of
that of the network. In this manner, the graph is obtained automatically; in fact, it is often unnecessary to draw the graph since it
can be visualized directly in the network itself. Since the flow graph
can be evaluated by inspection and by enumeration of the loops, the
input or transfer admittances or impedances, or the transfer functions
can be obtained directly from the network itself.

Instead of using Mason's rule to solve the flow graph, Robichaud[20]
has established a convenient rule for expanding the network determinants as a function of the elements. This rule can be applied
directly to the network itself without drawing the graph. For passive networks, this method is therefore equivalent to Kirchhoff's
rules[21] or to topological methods[22]. However, the method is more
general than purely topological methods because it can also be applied to active and nonreciprocal networks as well as to those containing mutual inductances.

3-2 NORMALIZED FLOW GRAPHS

For a given network, or one defined by its admittance or impedance matrix, in general several different graphs can be drawn to
represent the electrical equilibrium equations. Only one graph, which
will be called a *normalized graph* for reasons which will become
obvious, will retain our attention in this chapter. This normalized
graph will be considered as being of type N if the nodal voltages
are used as the variables, or of type M if the nodes of the graph
represent variables defined as the mesh currents.

3-2-1. Normalized flow graph of type N. For the flow graphs of type N, the voltages of the network nodes are defined as the potential differences between these nodes and a reference node. Kirchhoff's current law expresses the sum of the currents at node k as being null, that is:

$$0 = \sum_p J_{pk} + \sum_j i_{jk} = \sum_p J_{pk} + \sum_j y_{kj}(e_j - e_k) \qquad p, j \neq k \qquad (3\text{-}1)$$

$$0 = \sum_p J_{pk} + \sum_j y_{kj}e_j - e_k \sum_j y_{kj} \qquad\qquad p, j \neq k \qquad (3\text{-}2)$$

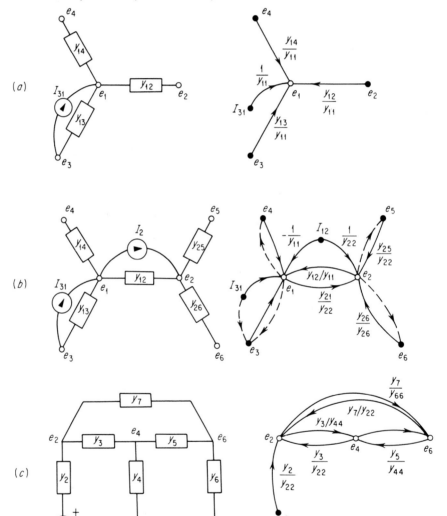

Fig. 3-1. Normalized graph of type N

Rewriting this as:

$$e_k = \sum_p \frac{J_{pk}}{y_{kk}} + \sum_j \frac{y_{kj}}{y_{kk}} e_j \qquad (3\text{-}3)$$

with:

$$y_{kk} = \sum_j y_{kj} \qquad (3\text{-}4)$$

the graph of Fig. 3-1a is obtained for the given subnetwork. This figure defines the symbols of the preceding equations.

By applying Kirchhoff's current law to the other nodes of the network, the graph can be completed. For example, in Fig. 3-1b the graph in solid lines represents the application of Kirchhoff's equations to the first two nodes of the network, and the dotted lines suggest the representation of the additional equations for the other nodes.

Expressing these equations in matrix form gives:

$$J = YE \qquad (3\text{-}5)$$

J is a column matrix whose k'th element is the current applied to node k of the network. E is the column matrix of the potential differences between the network nodes and the reference node. The admittance matrix Y is the parameter matrix of the nodal equations of the network. It is a square matrix of order n equal to the number of nodes in the (simply connected) network minus one. By writing Y in the form: $Y = N + T =$

$$
\begin{bmatrix}
y_{11} & -y_{12} & \cdots & -y_{1n} \\
-y_{21} & y_{22} & \cdots & -y_{2n} \\
\cdot & \cdot & & \cdot \\
\cdot & \cdot & & \cdot \\
\cdot & \cdot & & \cdot \\
-y_{n1} & -y_{n2} & & y_{nn}
\end{bmatrix}
$$

$$
=
\begin{bmatrix}
y_{11} & & & \\
& y_{22} & & \\
& & \cdot & \\
& & & \cdot \\
& & & y_{nn}
\end{bmatrix}
-
\begin{bmatrix}
0 & y_{12} & \cdots & y_{1n} \\
y_{21} & 0 & \cdots & y_{2n} \\
\cdot & \cdot & & \cdot \\
\cdot & \cdot & & \cdot \\
\cdot & \cdot & & \cdot \\
y_{n1} & y_{n2} & & 0
\end{bmatrix}
\qquad (3\text{-}6)
$$

the nodal admittances and the transfer admittances are separated. The nodal admittance y_{ii} at the i'th node is the admittance measured between the i'th node and the reference node when all the other nodes are short-circuited to the reference node. The transfer admittance y_{ij} is the admittance between the nodes i and j when all the other nodes are short-circuited to the reference node.

From the Eqs. (3-5) and (3-6) one writes:

$$J = YE = NE + TE \tag{3-7}$$

or:

$$N^{-1}J = E + N^{-1}TE \tag{3-8}$$

$$E = N^{-1}J - N^{-1}TE = \tag{3-9}$$

$$
\begin{bmatrix} e_1 \\ e_2 \\ \cdot \\ \cdot \\ \cdot \\ e_n \end{bmatrix}
=
\begin{bmatrix} J_1/y_{11} \\ J_2/y_{22} \\ \cdot \\ \cdot \\ \cdot \\ J_n/y_{nn} \end{bmatrix}
+
\begin{bmatrix}
0 & \dfrac{y_{12}}{y_{11}} & \cdots & \dfrac{y_{1n}}{y_{11}} \\[2mm]
\dfrac{y_{21}}{y_{22}} & 0 & & \dfrac{y_{2n}}{y_{22}} \\[2mm]
\cdot & & & \\
& & & \\
& & & \\
\dfrac{y_{n1}}{y_{nn}} & \dfrac{y_{n2}}{y_{nn}} & \cdots & 0
\end{bmatrix}
\begin{bmatrix} e_1 \\ e_2 \\ \cdot \\ \cdot \\ \cdot \\ e_n \end{bmatrix}
\tag{3-10}
$$

Each nodal equation is of the form of Eq. (3-3) given previously, and it is this system of equations which is represented in the normalized flow graph of the nodal equations. It is this graph which will be called the normalized N flow graph. Figure 3-1c represents the N type normalized flow graph for a complete network. In terms of graphs, the normalization consists of taking the equations in a certain order for defining the nodes of the graph and of writing only normalized transmittances. Because of this, there results a one-to-one correspondence between the normalized flow graph and the system of equations which it represents. It is to be noted that *in a normalized flow graph the same normalizing factor appears in the denominator of all the transmittances of the branches which converge at a node.* In the N type of flow graph, the normalization factor is the nodal admittance of the node considered.

3-2-2. *Normalized flow graph of type M.* To write the mesh equations, the currents of the simple meshes of a planar network are used, and for a nonplanar network, supplementary closed contours are added as required. For the k'th mesh, Kirchhoff's voltage law gives:

$$0 = \sum_p V_{pk} + \sum_j e_{jk} = \sum_p V_{pk} + \sum_j z_{kj}(i_j - i_k) \qquad p, j \neq k \tag{3-11}$$

$$0 = \sum_p V_{pk} + \sum_j z_{kj}i_j - i_k \sum_j z_{kj} \qquad\qquad p, j \neq k \tag{3-12}$$

or:

$$i_k = \sum_p \frac{V_{pk}}{z_{kk}} + \sum_j \frac{z_{kj}}{z_{kk}} i_j \tag{3-13}$$

where:

$$z_{kk} = \sum_j z_{kj} \tag{3-14}$$

The symbols are defined by Fig. 3-2a which shows a complete mesh of a subnetwork with the graph which corresponds to it.

By applying Eq. (3-13) to define successively the other nodes of the flow graph, as is suggested by Fig. 3-2b, the normalized flow graph of type M is obtained.

A normalized M flow graph is given in Fig. 3-2c for a complete

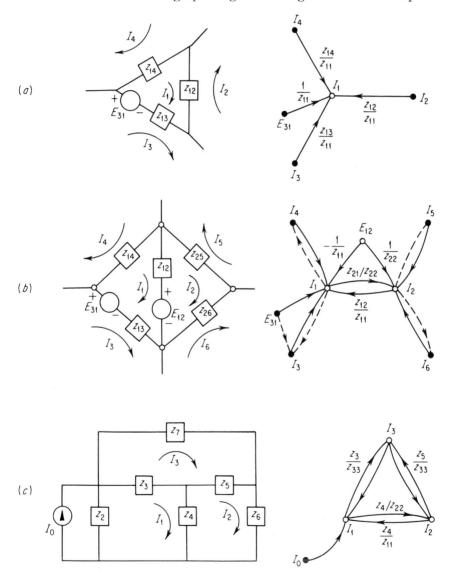

Fig. 3-2. Normalized graph of type M

network. The normalized flow graph represents the mesh equations written in a form which is the dual of that used for the nodal equations, that is:

$$
\begin{bmatrix} i_1 \\ i_2 \\ \cdot \\ \cdot \\ \cdot \\ i_n \end{bmatrix} = \begin{bmatrix} V_1/z_{11} \\ V_2/z_{22} \\ \cdot \\ \cdot \\ \cdot \\ V_n/z_{nn} \end{bmatrix} + \begin{bmatrix} 0 & \dfrac{z_{12}}{z_{22}} & \cdots & \dfrac{z_{1n}}{z_{11}} \\ \dfrac{z_{21}}{z_{22}} & 0 & & \cdot \\ \cdot & & & \cdot \\ \cdot & & & \cdot \\ \cdot & & & \cdot \\ \dfrac{z_{n1}}{z_{nn}} & \cdot & & 0 \end{bmatrix} \begin{bmatrix} i_1 \\ i_2 \\ \cdot \\ \cdot \\ \cdot \\ i_n \end{bmatrix} \qquad (3\text{-}15)
$$

3-2-3. *Properties of normalized flow graphs.* The normalized flow graph establishes a *one-to-one correspondence* between the system of equilibrium equations and the graph which represents these equations. There exists, in effect, only one normalized flow graph for a network in which the variables are defined, since it is necessary to take the variables in a given order; the k'th equation defining the k'th variable in the graph. The nodal admittances or the mesh impedances therefore become the normalizing factors, which appear only in the denominator of the transmittances. All the branches which converge towards the same node will have the same normalizing factor in the denominator.

In order to avoid all confusion with the matrix notation, it is to be noted that the branch i-k of the graph has in the expression of its transmittance the coefficient k-i of the system of equations. Except for the sources, the normalized flow graph of the nodal or mesh equations will always contain nodes which represent variables of the same nature, and which are equal in number to the number of the nodal or mesh equations.

In the N type graph, the nodes of the graph correspond to the nodes of the network, with the exception of the reference node, and are accessible for connecting sources. One can consider current sources connected between any pair of nodes, or voltage sources in which one terminal is connected to the reference node. Voltage sources which are connected to two arbitrary nodes other than the reference node will require first, that the geometry of the network be revised as it would be done in the usual method of writing the nodal equations. The dualistic situation applies for the M type of graphs where voltage sources can be placed in any mesh or, where current sources can be placed in the exterior contour of a planar network.

A normalized flow graph for an n-port network can also be drawn; it will be necessary to take the equations whose coefficients are the input and transfer functions for the variables defined at those n ports. The normalizing factors are then the input admittances or impedances of the n-port network, and the transmittances of the branches of the flow graph are the transfer functions divided by the normalizing factors of the (flow graph) nodes towards which these branches converge. This graph, which corresponds to the reduced equations, can be obtaind by the reduction of a detailed graph such as the one given in the example of Fig. 3-1c, according to the rules of reduction given previously. However, to obtain a normalized graph, it will be necessary to eliminate the simple loops obtained in the reduction process, in order to produce only normalized transmittances in the residual graph.

The expression for a desired variable can be obtained simply by inspection of the flow graph, using Mason's rule. Thus, in the example of Fig. 3-1c, the transfer function e_6 / E_1 can be written out directly:

$$\frac{e_6}{E_1} = \frac{1}{D} \frac{y_2}{y_{22}} \left[\frac{y_3 y_5}{y_{44} y_{66}} + \frac{y_7}{y_{66}} \right] \qquad (3\text{-}16)$$

The determinant of the flow graph is:

$$D = 1 - \frac{y_3^2}{y_{22} y_{44}} - \frac{y_5^2}{y_{44} y_{66}} - \frac{y_7^2}{y_{22} y_{66}} - \frac{2 y_3 y_5 y_7}{y_{22} y_{44} y_{66}} \qquad (3\text{-}17)$$

The Eq. (3-16) is simplified if the numerator and denominator are multiplied through by all the normalizing factors:

$$\frac{e_6}{E_1} = \frac{y_2 y_3 y_5 + y_7 y_{44}}{\Delta} \qquad (3\text{-}18)$$

where

$$\Delta = y_{22} y_{44} y_{66} D \qquad (3\text{-}19)$$

Δ is the determinant of the system of (nodal) equations of the network and differs from the flow graph determinant by a factor which will always be the product of all the normalizing factors.

3-3 INDEFINITE FLOW GRAPHS

There is an evident relationship between the structure of the normalized flow graph and that of the network whose equilibrium equations are represented by the graph. In the case of indefinite normalized graphs, this relation between the flow graph and the network can be illustrated more completely. At the same time, a very direct method will be established for obtaining a normalized graph which corresponds to a given network, without having to consider the equations, even implicitly.

3-3-1. *Indefinite N flow graphs.* Instead of considering the *N* flow graph as the superposition of subgraphs, each of which corresponds to one nodal equation as in Fig. 3-1a, the graph can be visualized as composed of elementary structures which are loops of two branches. Thus, the graph is obtained by drawing a loop of two branches for each admittance of the network as shown in Fig. 3-3a. The transmittances of these two branches of the flow graph are equal to the admittance of the corresponding branch of the network divided by the normalization factor (equal to the nodal admittance of the node towards which the branches are directed).

If one of the nodes at the end of a branch of the graph is a voltage source (of infinite admittance), the branches converging towards this node can be removed, since the total admittance at this node becomes infinite and it appears in the denominator of the transmittances. Thus, in the network of Fig. 3-3c, the graph is obtained directly, and the branches shown in dotted lines are not necessary because their transmittances are zero. If there are current sources in the network, source nodes can be added in the flow graph with branches whose transmittances are equal to the inverse of the normalization factor (Fig. 3-3b). The normalized flow graph is thus obtained:

1. by considering the branches of the network which are connected to the reference node as being connected to this node by voltage sources of infinite admittance and of value zero if they do not appear initially in the network (that is generalized short-circuits).

2. by replacing each branch of the network by a loop of two branches in the graph, as shown in Fig. 3-3a.

3. by replacing each current source by a source node in the graph connected to the appropriate nodes of the graph as shown in Fig. 3-3b.

The graph corresponding to the indicated network has been drawn in Fig. 3-3c according to the procedures described previously. The branches drawn as dotted lines are not necessary, either because their transmittances are zero (due to an infinite admittance in the denominator), or because the source node from which they emanate is zero. The graph drawn in solid lines is the N graph obtained previously for the same network in Fig. 3-1c.

By neglecting the sources, and by connecting all the dotted branches to the reference node, the graph of Fig. 3-3c becomes the

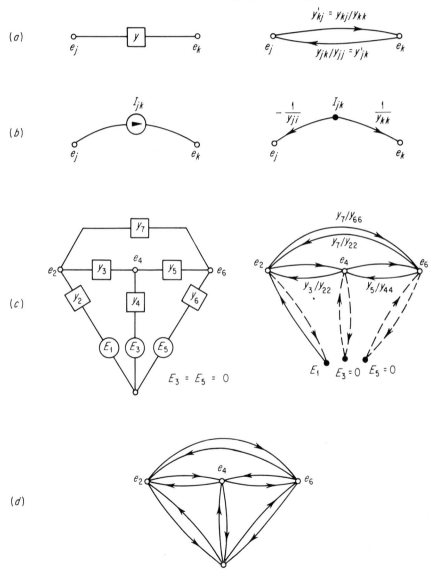

Fig. 3-3. Direct method of derivation of the N graph

indefinite N flow graph. This graph is a loop graph consisting exclusively of loops with two branches, each loop corresponding to one of the branches of the network; the graph contains exactly the same number of nodes as the network. If the nodes of the flow graph are arranged in a manner identical to that of the nodes of the network, a geometry or topology identical to that of the network is obtained for the indefinite graph, provided each loop of two branches is considered as one element.

At any node in the indefinite flow graph, the sum of the numerators of the transmittances of all incoming branches is always equal to the sum of the numerators of the outgoing branches. In the indefinite N flow graph, this sum is also equal to the nodal admittance of the node considered.

3-3-2. *Indefinite Matrices.* Consider a network with a total number n_t of nodes. If e_k designates the voltage difference between node k and a reference node taken outside of the network and J_{pk} the current source between the nodes p and k, n_t equations of the type 3–3 can be written for the n_t nodes of the network. The matrix of this system of nodal equations has been called indefinite admittance matrix by Shekel[23] and will be designated here by Y_i. This matrix is singular because there exist only n independent potential differences in the network and n independent nodal equations. It can be easily verified that the sum of the elements of any row or of any column of this matrix Y_i is always zero. The flow graph obtained above was called indefinite because it represents this indefinite matrix in its normalized form.

In the indefinite N flow graph, the sum of the numerators of the transmittances of the branches which converge at or diverge from any node is equal to the nodal admittance because the sum of the elements of the corresponding row or column of Y_i is zero.

If a node in the network is chosen as the reference node, one of the n_t potential differences considered above (in a simply connected network) is cancelled. One of the columns of the indefinite matrix therefore disappears because all the coefficients are multiplied by zero. The row corresponding to this column can also be removed because only n independent equations are required. Similarly, in the flow graph, if a node of the indefinite graph is chosen as "reference," that is as a zero (voltage) source, the branches which converge at this node disappear because this node represents an independent variable. The branches which diverge from this node are also removed since the source is of value zero. The specification of a reference node thus removes a node of the indefinite graph and all the branches which were attached to this node. Conversely, if a row and a column are added in the definite matrix so as to make the sum of the elements in each column and row zero, the indefinite matrix is reproduced. In the definite flow graph, if an extra node and loops with two branches are added such that the sum of the numerators of the transmittances of the branches which converge towards any node is equal to the sum of the numerators of the transmittances of the branches diverging from that node, the indefinite graph is reproduced.

The mesh equations of a network can be dealt with by proceeding in the same manner. The indefinite impedance matrix Z_i will contain an extra row and column. If the l currents in the l simple meshes of a planar network are chosen as the independent variables, the dualistic situation of that which existed in the preceding study by the nodal method will result. The additional elements of the indefinite matrix Z_i come from the external mesh of the network (drawn in a direction opposite to that of the internal meshes) which corresponds to the reference node of the nodal equations. A planar network can, in effect, be drawn on a plane in such a way that any region can be the exterior region[24]. In this way, there does not exist a priori a preference for defining one mesh rather than another as the exterior mesh, in the same way as in the nodal method there is not a priori a preference for defining one node rather than another as the reference node. In a nonplanar network, an indefinite impedance matrix can still be written. The closed contour to which the additional elements of the indefinite matrix correspond will still be called the external mesh of the network, although topologically the exterior mesh for the nonplanar network cannot be uniquely defined.

3-3-3. Indefinite M flow graphs. If the mesh equations are written in the form of Eq. (3-15) for the indefinite impedance matrix for the $(l + 1)$ meshes of the network including the external mesh, an indefinite (normalized) M flow graph is obtained. For a planar network, this indefinite flow graph will have a structure which is the dual of the network. Each of the $(l + 1)$ meshes of the network corresponds to a node of the flow graph, and each branch of the network has at least one corresponding loop of two branches in the flow graph. The transmittances of these branches are the corresponding impedances of the branches of the network divided by the total impedance of the mesh relative to the node of the flow graph towards which these branches are directed. The graph of Fig. 3–4d for the network of Fig. 3–2c is thereby obtained. The relation between the graph and the network has been illustrated by drawing the graph in a configuration dualistic to that of the network. For a nonplanar network, meshes will be drawn in the planar part of the network and one or more additional contours will be added for the nonplanar part. An exterior mesh (as defined before) is also used. The indefinite graph consists of a loop of two branches for each impedance which is common to two meshes when all possible combinations of meshes taken two at a time are considered. The resultant structure of the indefinite graph in the case of a nonplanar network has already been defined as dualistic to that of the network, using a generalized definition of duality[25].

The choice of l independent meshes among the $(l + 1)$ meshes used requires the removal of one flow graph node and all the branches attached to it to obtain a definite graph. This operation is analogous to that which consists of removing a row and the corresponding column in the indefinite matrix Z_i to obtain the impedance matrix.

The definite M graph will contain only loops with two branches if all the sources are ignored. The graph can thus be assembled by superimposing a loop of two branches for each impedance of the network which is common to two mesh currents, as shown in Fig. 3–4a. If one of the two currents is a source (of infinite impedance), one of the branches of this loop disappears because its transmittance becomes zero, the denominator which is the total mesh impedance being infinite. A voltage source of the network becomes a source node in the graph, and the transmittance of each of the branches which leave the source node is the inverse of the mesh impedance of the node which these branches enter.

In a manner similar to that used for the N flow graph, a direct procedure can be given for obtaining the definite M flow graph:

1. The branches of the exterior mesh of the network will be considered to be connected in parallel to current sources; these sources have infinite impedance and a value of zero if they are not required (thus being considered as generalized open-circuits).

2. Each mesh current of the network will be made to correspond to a node of the flow graph and the impedances common to two meshes will be replaced by a flow graph loop of two

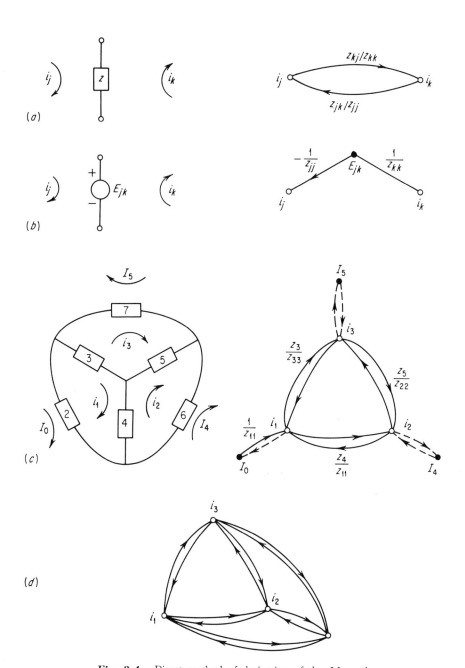

Fig. 3-4. Direct method of derivation of the M graph

branches as shown in Fig. 3–4a. If there are more than two currents in an impedance of the network, all possible pairs of currents will be considered in turn.

3. Each voltage source of the network will be represented by a source node in the flow graph; the branches diverging from this node have transmittances equal to the inverse (except for signs) of the mesh impedance relative to the node to which these branches converge. This is shown in Fig. 3–4b.

This procedure has been applied to Fig. 3–4c to obtain the graph of the corresponding network. The loops drawn in dotted lines disappear in the definite graph as was explained for the N type of graph. If there exists a current source such as I_0 in Fig. 3–4c, this current source becomes a source in the graph. If the nodes corresponding to the external meshes are joined together, the indefinite graph of Fig. 3–4d is obtained.

3-4 BIDIRECTIONAL GRAPHS

Although Mason's Nonintersecting-Loop rule is sufficient to calculate any particular transfer function in the normalized graph, the normalization inherent in this type of graph leads to expressions which contain denominators. Furthermore, as has been indicated in Eqs. (3–16) and (3–17), the normalization factors disappear when the expressions obtained by Mason's rule are reduced. Also, the determinant of the graph differs from the determinant of the admittance or impedance matrix of the network by a factor which is the product of all of the normalization factors. These normalization factors can be completely eliminated if a new type of graph, that will be called a bidirectional graph, is introduced. It will be possible with this graph to obtain an expansion of the determinant of the network, in terms of the admittances or impedances of the branches of the network, instead of an expression in terms of the loop transmittances of the flow graph. Furthermore, this expansion gives a final expression for the determinant, whereas the Laplace expansion would produce many additional terms which would cancel.

3-4-1. Definition and properties of the bidirectional graph. The bidirectional graph is a topological representation of the normalized flow graph. In this new graph, the loops with two branches of the flow graph become single branches with arrows in both directions. The single branches in the flow graph are not modified. Instead of writing the normalized transmittances, only the numerators of the flow graph transmittances without their normalization factors will be written in the bidirectional graph. These factors are nevertheless contained in the graph, since it is necessary only to sum the coefficients associated with the converging or diverging branches at any node in the bidirectional graph to obtain the nodal admittance or the mesh impedance at any node of the graph. The two arrows on a bidirectional branch will have the same coefficient if this branch corresponds to a bilateral element, and two coefficients otherwise. The coefficient in the first case is simply the admittance or impedance of the corresponding branch of the network; for a branch representing a nonreciprocal element, two coefficients, which are the two transfer admittances or impedances of the nonreciprocal branch, will be required.

All the normalized flow graphs already considered in this chapter can be represented in the form of a bidirectional graph. Thus, a bidirectional graph can be definite or indefinite depending on whether or not a node is included to represent the reference node for the N type of graph or the external mesh for the M type of graph.

As with the indefinite matrices[26], the indefinite bidirectional graph of several subnetworks can be directly connected together to obtain the graph for the complete network. With the (normalized) flow graphs, it is necessary to change the transmittances of the branches of the subnetworks which are connected together, since the normalization factors (nodal admittances or mesh impedances) are modified by the interconnection of the subnetworks. In the bidirectional graph, it is not necessary to be concerned with the normalization factors. These can be obtained by inspection of the bidirectional graph (for example, if it is desired to relate it to a flow graph) by summing all coefficients which converge at or diverge from any node.

The transformations or operations already established for flow graphs are still valid for the bidirectional graphs; it is necessary to remember that the coefficients of the branches of the bidirectional graphs must be divided by the appropriate normalization factors to calculate the residual transmittances, and that these should in turn be denormalized for the residual bidirectional graph. It is possible, in this way, to start from a detailed bidirectional graph for a network, and to obtain a reduced bidirectional graph corresponding to the reduced equations (for example at the open terminals) of this network.

The bidirectional graphs are a topological representation of the

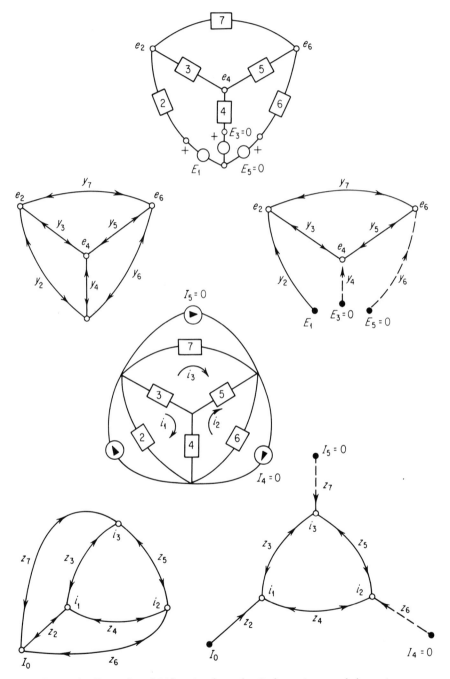

Fig. 3-5. Examples of bidirectional graphs (indeterminate and determinate, of types N and M)

equations because they represent symbolically the flow graphs associated with this system of equations. Furthermore, an indefinite bidirectional graph of type N will represent all the nodes of the network and its structure will be identical to that of the topological graph of the network. An indefinite M type bidirectional graph will have a geometry dualistic to that of the topological graph in the case of a planar network. Examples of bidirectional graphs are given in Fig. 3-5.

3-4-2. *Expansion rule.* (*1*) *Network determinant.* The direct expansion of the determinant of the network can be made starting from any node of the indefinite bidirectional graph. If the coefficients of the branches which diverge from this starting node and which converge towards the nodes $1, 2, \ldots i$, are called $a_1, a_2, \ldots a_i$, the determinant of the network can be expressed by:

$$\Delta = \sum a_i \Delta_i + \sum a_i a_j \Delta_{ij} + \sum a_i a_j a_k \Delta_{ijk} + \ldots \qquad (3\text{-}20)$$

In the products $a_i a_j a_k \ldots$, it is necessary to take all possible combinations of these branches. The $\Delta_{ijk}\ldots$ are the determinants of subgraphs. These subgraphs are obtained from the original graph by removing all the branches a_i and also all the branches which are connected between the nodes indicated by the indices of the corresponding $\Delta_{ijk}\ldots$. The node obtained by the superposition of the nodes $ijk\ldots$ will then be considered as the new reference node for the calculation of the determinant of the subgraph. This calculation is done by using the preceeding Eq. (3-20) in the subgraph. An example is given in detail in Fig. 3-6, and the subgraphs corresponding to a few terms have been drawn.

The starting reference node for this expansion of the determinant is arbitrary[27, 28, 29]; it will be advantageous, for passive networks, to choose a node having a large number of outgoing branches. Instead of taking the a_i as the diverging branches, the branches which converge to the reference node could have been chosen for the calculation of the determinant; in general it will be necessary, however, to proceed in the same manner for the determinants of the subnetworks.

It is also possible to expand the determinant of the network with respect to one of the coefficients of any branch of the bidirectional graph. Let a_{ij} be the coefficient of this branch; the determinant will then be expressed by:

$$\Delta = a_{ij} \Delta_{ij} + \Delta^{a_{ij}} \qquad (3\text{-}21)$$

In this expression:

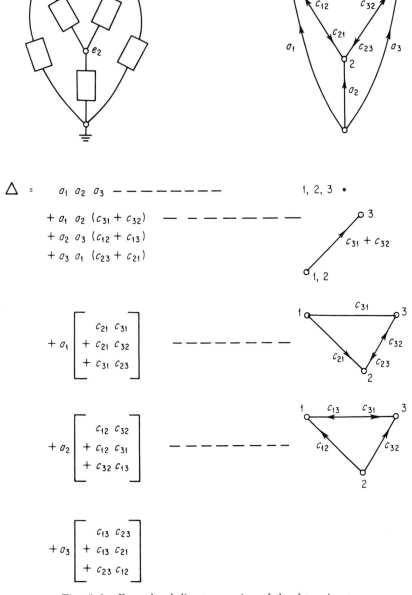

Fig. 3-6. Example of direct expansion of the determinant

Δ_{ij} is the determinant calculated by Eq. (3-20) in a subgraph where the branch a_{ij} has been removed, and where the nodes at the ends of a_{ij} have been superimposed in a single node.

$\Delta^{a_{ij}}$ is the determinant calculated by Eq. (3-20) in a subgraph with the branch a_{ij} removed.

It will thus be necessary to expand these determinants starting from node i. If desired, the determinants of these subgraphs can be expanded with respect to another branch attached to node j by using again Eq. (3-21). In this manner, it is possible to expand the determinant with respect to a given group of branches.

The expansion rule is established in the appendix; it is also shown there that Eq. (3-20) is an expansion of the determinant of the matrix of the equilibrium equations in terms of the excesses of the elements of the principal diagonal of the matrix. These excesses, being the differences between the element kk of a row or of a column and the sum of the other elements of the same row or column, are thus the negatives of the elements situated in the additional column or row in the indefinite matrix.

(2) *Expression for any variable.* The expression of any variable x_j in a bidirectional graph where there is only one source x_0 will be given by an expression analogous to that of Mason's rule:

$$\frac{x_j}{x_0} = \sum_r \frac{c_r \Delta_r}{\Delta} \qquad (3\text{-}22)$$

where:

c_r represents the product of the branch coefficients of the rth open path $x_0 - x_j$ in the bidirectional graph,

Δ_r is the determinant calculated for a subgraph obtained from the original graph by superimposing to the reference node all those nodes encountered in the rth open path,

Δ is the determinant of the network.

These determinants can of course be calculated by Eq. (3-20) in the bidirectional graph. If there are several sources, their effects are combined by superposition.

However, because of the simple relation which exists between the structure of the bidirectional graph and that of the network, the formulas given above can be applied directly to the networks themselves. This is true for all the reciprocal networks studied by the nodal method because the bidirectional graph has the same structure as the network. It is still true in the planar reciprocal networks studied by the mesh method, since the bidirectional graph has a geometry dual to that of the network. This geometry can be visualized with the aid of a graphical procedure of constructing the dual network, described for example by Guillemin[30].

3-5 ACTIVE AND NONRECIPROCAL ELEMENTS AND MUTUAL INDUCTANCES

The graphs considered in this chapter can also be applied to general networks, as well as to the passive reciprocal networks without mutual coupling which have been considered so far. In these passive networks, the drawing of the graph is immediate because of the simple relation which exists between the structure of the graph and that of the network; indeed, it is not necessary to draw the graph if it is visualized in the network. For networks containing active or nonreciprocal elements or mutual inductances, or for an *n*-port network, it will be necessary in general to draw the graph. This graph, in effect, can have a structure which an equivalent network or an *n*-port network cannot suggest. To draw the graph in this case, a subnetwork of *n* terminals will be imagined and considered to be connected to the rest of the network by these *n* terminals. It will suffice to determine the graph of these *n*-port subnetworks and to connect them to the graph of the other part of the network.

3-5-1. Indefinite graphs of n-port networks. The indefinite graph of an *n*-port network can be obtained by starting from an equivalent network for which a flow graph is drawn. This graph can then be reduced, by the reduction methods already given, to a normalized graph containing only the nodes for the terminal variables.

In the example of the triode of Fig. 3-7, a flow graph can be drawn directly from the equivalent circuit of Fig. 3-7a. To obtain a flow graph of the nodal equations, it is necessary first to eliminate the node i_p as shown in Fig. 3-7b. The normalized graph is then obtained by the reduction of the loop at node e_2 by modifying the transmittances of the branches which converge at this node. This places in evidence in the denominator the nodal admittance y'_{22} which is equal to the sum of the admittances connected to the node and of the g_m of the triode. Fig. 3-7c shows the indefinite N flow graph and the bidirectional N graph.

In the case of the cathode follower of Fig. 3-8a, for which the graph is immediately formed from the subgraphs of the passive element and the triode, one obtains:

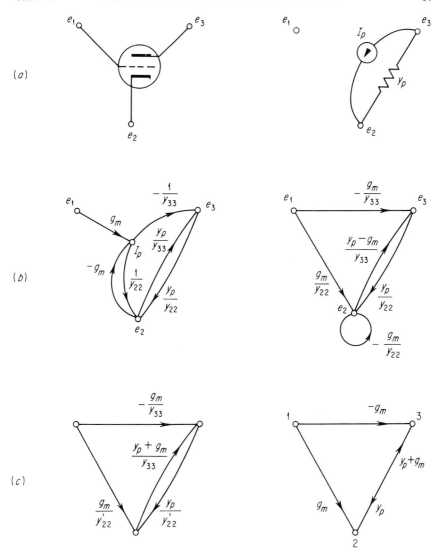

Fig. 3-7. N graphs for the triode

$$e_2 = \frac{g_m E_1 + y_p E_3 + y_k E_4}{g_m + y_p + y_k} \qquad (3\text{-}23)$$

For the general amplifier of Fig. 3–8b, where the admittances of the branches are designated by $a, b, c, \dots h$, the bidirectional graph is first drawn for the passive part of the network, and then the bidirectional N graph already obtained for the triode is added to produce the over-all bidirectional graph shown in Fig. 3–8b. Any desired result can be obtained from this graph. For example, the transfer function from input to output becomes:

$$\frac{e_3}{E_0} = \frac{a(b - g_m)y_{22} + (d + g_m)(k + g_m)}{\Delta} \tag{3-24}$$

where Δ is the determinant of the network. This determinant is obtained by the expansion rule which was given above, for example by making the expansion relative to node 3 (with $n = a + f$ and $k = y_p + c$):

$$\begin{aligned}
\Delta = {}&bkh + bk(n + g) + bh(d + g_m + g) + kh(n + d) \\
&+ b[n(d + g_m) + ng + (d + g_m)g] \\
&+ k(dg + dn + gn) + h[ng + n(d + g_m) + gd] \tag{3-25}
\end{aligned}$$

If the determinant is expanded relative to a node different from

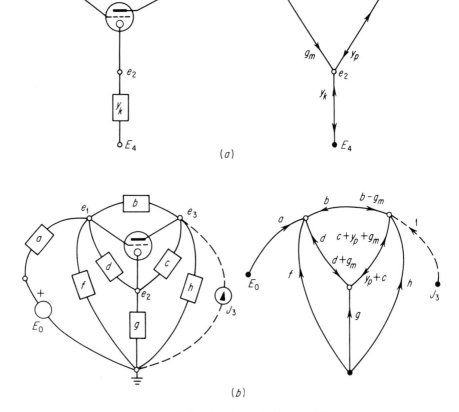

(a)

(b)

Fig. 3-8. Bidirectional graphs for amplifiers
$n = a + f, \quad k = y_p + c$

node 3, it will be necessary to write more terms than those given above, and then to simplify the negative terms which come from the coefficient $(b - g_m)$. The expression for the transfer function could be obtained by applying Mason's rule to the definite flow graph derived from the bidirectional graph of Fig. 3-8b, by removing node 4 and the branches connected to it. However, this method would lead to a large number of terms, many of which would cancel one another. The output impedance of the amplifier can be obtained by removing the source E_0 from the graph, and by considering the current source J_3 shown in dotted lines in the bidirectional graph. The output impedance Z_{33} is obtained by the application of the expansion rule for the ratio:

$$\frac{e_{33}}{J_3} = Z_{33} = \frac{\Delta_{33}}{\Delta} \qquad (3\text{-}26)$$

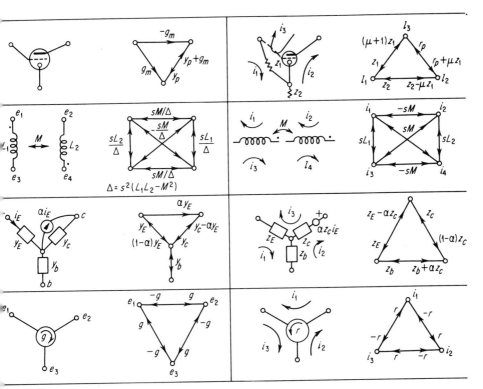

Fig. 3-9. Table of indeterminate bidirectional graphs of types N and M for some elements

where Δ is the determinant of the network calculated previously. Δ_{33} is the determinant of the subgraph obtained by superimposing node 3 to the reference node, and also by removing those branches connecting node 3 to the reference node. We therefore obtain:

$$\Delta_{33} = (n + b)(g + k) + (n + b)(d + g_m) + (g + k)d \quad (3\text{-}27)$$

If the indefinite graphs of n-port networks are given, it is necessary only to attach these graphs onto the indefinite graph of the rest of the network to obtain the complete graph. The indefinite bidirectional graphs for several n-port networks which are frequently encountered have been grouped in a table (Fig. 3-9).

For an n-port network, it is also possible, if desired, to derive the indefinite graphs directly from its admittance or impedance matrices. A definite graph corresponding to this matrix can be drawn and the graph rendered indefinite by the addition of a node and branches, such that at any node the sum of the coefficients of the convergent branches are equal to the sum of the coefficients of the divergent branches (in the bidirectional graph). Alternatively, the indefinite matrix can be written by adding one row and one column such that the sum of the elements of any row and of any column is zero; the indefinite graph can then be drawn from it.

For the gyrator of Fig. 3-9 for example, determined by its admittance matrix:

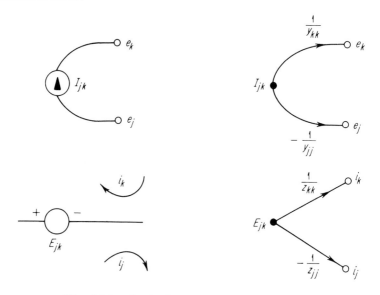

Fig. 3-10. Graphs for current and voltage sources

$$Y = \begin{bmatrix} 0 & g \\ -g & 0 \end{bmatrix} \tag{3-28}$$

one can write for the indefinite matrix the equations:

$$\begin{bmatrix} J_1 \\ J_2 \\ J_3 \end{bmatrix} = \begin{bmatrix} 0 & g & -g \\ -g & 0 & g \\ g & -g & 0 \end{bmatrix} \begin{bmatrix} e_1 \\ e_2 \\ e_3 \end{bmatrix} \tag{3-29}$$

and the indefinite bidirectional N graph of Fig. 3-9 follows immediately.

3-5-2. *Indefinite Graphs of Dependent Sources.* For active networks, which can always be represented as a passive network with dependent sources[31], the normalized graph can be obtained in a direct manner if the graph corresponding to the dependent sources is drawn, since the passive (reciprocal) part of the equivalent circuit has a graph whose structure is identical to that of the network or its dual. Consider subgraphs which correspond to current and voltage sources (Fig. 3-10) and the graphs (Fig. 3-11) which represent the measurement of a current or of a voltage. To obtain the indefinite graph of dependent sources, it will suffice to connect together these two types of graphs to represent a source which depends on a current or a voltage measured somewhere in a network. The flow graphs of all possible dependent sources are assembled in the table of Fig. 3-12.

It happens often that one of the nodes between which the source

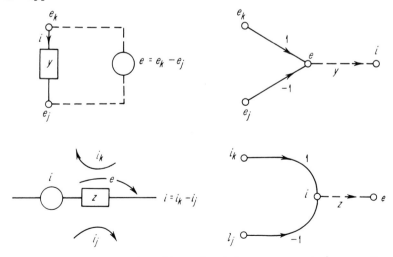

Fig. 3-11. Representation with graphs of the measurement of a current or a voltage

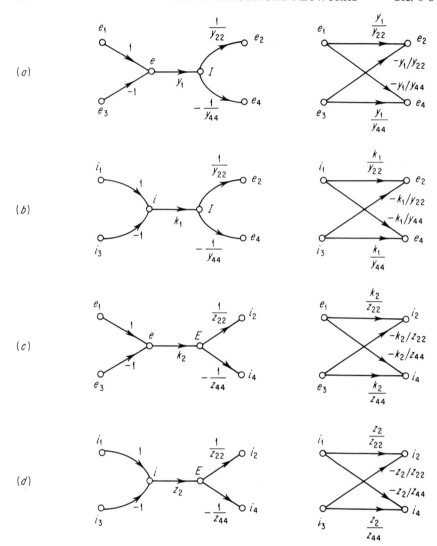

Fig. 3-12. Flow graphs of sources dependent on a current or on a voltage

is applied is the same as one of the nodes which represents a variable on which the source depends. This causes no trouble with the graphs already obtained, since it suffices to superimpose those two nodes and to reduce the flow graph by the methods of reduction. Thus, for the triode for which the current source connected between the plate and the cathode depends on the voltage measured between the grid and the cathode, the graph of Fig. 3-12a will be used, with nodes e_3 and e_4 superimposed to obtain the bidirectional graph already shown in Fig. 3-7c (in which g_p is ignored if it is desired to see only the effect of the dependent source and $g_m = -y$).

If the bidirectional graphs are used instead of the flow graphs, it is necessary only to superimpose the two nodes and to remove the simple loops which may result. Since the denominators no longer appear in the coefficients of the branches of the bidirectional graph, the reduction of a loop is no longer a required operation.

If a voltage source is considered to be connected between two meshes and is dependent on the current which circulates between these meshes, then the resultant flow graph will be obtained by the superposition of nodes i_1 and i_2, and also of i_3 and i_4 in the graph of Fig. 3-12d. This graph reduces to a normalized graph having two branches whose numerators are z_2. In the case in which z_2 is positive, a graph of two branches is obtained, corresponding to a bilateral element of a network as shown in Fig. 3-4a. This, therefore, serves to demonstrate the theorem of substition: "in a network, a passive impedance z can be replaced by a voltage source zi where i is the current which flows in that impedance." In the case in which z_2 is negative, it is thus shown that a negative impedance can be represented by a dependent source.

3-6 ANALYSIS WITH MIXED VARIABLES

The term mixed—or hybrid—equations will be applied to the equilibrium equations obtained when part of a network has been studied by the mesh method and the other part by the nodal method of analysis. The current variables for part of the network are defined when the (network) nodes for the other part are short-circuited to the reference node, and conversely, the voltage variables in one part of the network are defined when the meshes are opened in the other part. In other words, each parameter, in any method of analysis, is obtained by considering all variables to be zero except those required to evaluate this parameter.

In the mixed method of analysis the variables are, of course, not homogeneous. This method is easy to use with flow graphs; it should be used whenever it is felt that the resulting graph would be simplified. It will also be necessary to use it if an element of a network or of a subnetwork is already defined in terms of mixed parameters. The mixed method of analysis will first be illustrated by the use of simple examples; indefinite hybrid graphs will then be briefly described.

3-6-1. *Applications of mixed analysis.* The complexity of a flow graph depends on the number of nodes of the graph, but it is even more dependent on the number of loops and the degree of coupling between these loops. A measure of the complexity of the graph is the index as defined in the first chapter. It can happen that the index of a graph can be greatly reduced in a hybrid

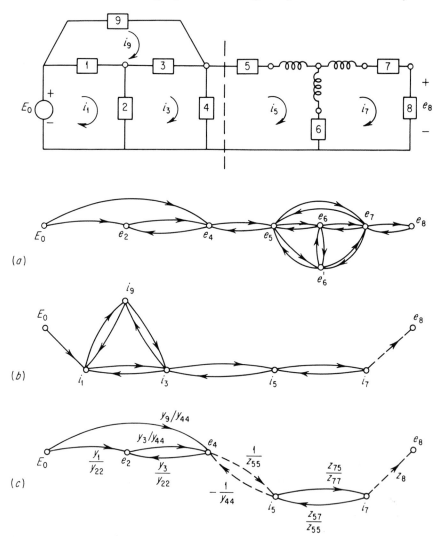

Fig. 3-13. Graphs of types N, M, and H for a network

graph as compared to the index of a graph of type N or M. Thus, for the network of Fig. 3–13 the normalized N graph of Fig. 3–13a is of index 4, whereas the mesh flow graph of Fig. 3–13b has an index of 3. If the network is cut ‚at the dotted line, the two resulting subnetworks can be represented immediately in the form of an N and of an M graph as shown in the heavy lines of Fig. 3–13c. The subgraphs are connected together by considering the current i_5 as an equivalent source connected to the network on the left of the dotted line, and the voltage e_4 as an equivalent voltage source for the network at the right.

The branches indicated by dotted lines are thus obtained and the graph becomes a normalized hybrid or H type of flow graph. The normalizing factors at all voltage nodes are admittances and at all current nodes are impedances. In the definite flow graph, Mason's rule can be used to obtain the transfer function e_8 / E_0, for example, in terms of the branch transmittances of the graph, as follows:

$$\frac{e_8}{E_0} = \frac{\dfrac{1}{Z_{55}} \dfrac{Z_{75}}{Z_{77}} \left[\dfrac{Y_1}{Y_{22}} \dfrac{Y_3}{Y_{44}} + \dfrac{Y_9}{Y_{44}} \right] Z_8}{1 - \dfrac{Y_3^2}{Y_{22} Y_{44}} - \dfrac{Z_{57} Z_{75}}{Z_{55} Z_{77}} + \dfrac{1}{Z_{55} Y_{44}} + \dfrac{Y_3^2 Z_{75} Z_{57}}{Y_{22} Y_{44} Z_{55} Z_{77}}} \qquad (3\text{–}30)$$

Another example is given in Fig. 3–14. This network consists of two subnetworks, designated by A and B in the diagram, and of a two-port network N defined by its matrix h. To avoid inversion of

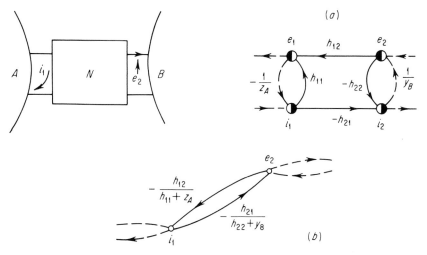

Fig. 3-14. Quadripole specified by its matrix h and corresponding graph of type H

this matrix, it is necessary to use mixed variables. The two-port network is represented by the flow graph in solid lines in Fig. 3-14a, and the voltage e_1 at the terminal of network A can be considered as a voltage source if network A is treated on a mesh basis. In the same manner, the current at the output of the quadripole is treated as a current source for network B for which the nodal method would be used. The nodes e_1 and e_2 can be eliminated to obtain the residual graph of Fig. 3-14b. The part to the left of node i_1 in the graph will contain only current nodes, and the normalizing factors will be mesh impedances. It should be noted that the impedance of the last mesh of network A is increased by h_{11} the input impedance of the quadripole. For node e_2 and the other voltage nodes of network B, the normalizing factors are the nodal admittances. At node e_2, the nodal admittance is h_{22} plus the nodal admittance of the first node of network B.

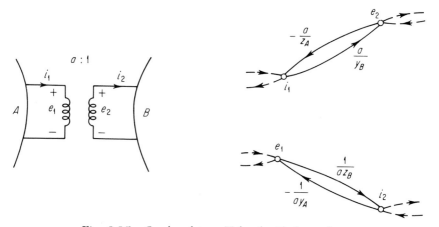

Fig. 3-15. Graphs of type H for the ideal transformer

The ideal transformer of Fig. 3-15 is a particular case of the quadripole described above. If the normalized flow graph for the transformer alone is desired, then it is necessary to use mixed variables.

3-6-2. Indefinite mixed matrices. In order to make use of the expansion rules of Sec. 3-4 in the hybrid graphs, it is necessary to draw the indeterminate hybrid graphs corresponding to the (normalized) indefinite mixed matrices. It is first necessay to define the mixed variables. Their choice can be made in many ways. For a general representation, an n-port network with ideal transformers of unity

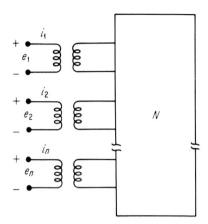

Fig. 3-16. n-port Network

turns ratio at each terminal is considered (Fig. 3–16). This representation is valid for a detailed study, such as the one which was done for the network of Fig. 3–14, provided that a pair of terminals is produced for each mesh of the subnetwork on the left by making a cut in this mesh, and that a pair of terminals is produced for each pair of nodes of the subnetwork on the right by connecting two wires to these nodes.

The network N of Fig. 3–16 is subdivided into two networks N_y and N_z which are studied by the nodal and mesh methods respectively. For the moment, these subnetworks are uniquely defined by the subdivision of the terminal-pairs into two distinct groups. To the first group are associated voltage variables and to the second group dependent current variables. These are designated by column matrices E and I. The current sources which are applied to the terminal pairs of the first group must be taken as sources for the nodal system of equations; they are represented by the column matrix J. By duality, the potentials applied to the terminals of the second group are considered as equivalent voltage sources for the mesh system of equations; they will be designated by the column matrix V. One can therefore write for the network N_y:

$$J = YE + MI \qquad (3\text{-}31)$$

where the term MI represents the effect of the network N_z on N_y, the mesh currents of network N_z acting as equivalent current sources for N_y. In the same manner, one has for network N_z:

$$V = NE + ZI \qquad (3\text{-}32)$$

By grouping together these two equations, the hybrid matrix H is obtained:

$$\begin{bmatrix} J \\ V \end{bmatrix} = \begin{bmatrix} Y & M \\ N & Z \end{bmatrix} \begin{bmatrix} E \\ I \end{bmatrix} = H \begin{bmatrix} E \\ I \end{bmatrix} \qquad (3\text{-}33)$$

If, after opening the terminals of the subnetwork N_z, $(n + 1)$, terminal-pairs are defined for the n independent potential differences of the subnetwork N_y, the matrix Y is the indefinite admittance matrix. Similarly, if, with the terminals of the subnetwork N_y short-circuited $(l + 1)$, terminal-pairs are defined for the l independent mesh currents of the subnetwork N_z, the matrix Z is an indefinite impedance matrix. The matrix H, in this case, is therefore also an indefinite matrix, and the sum of any row or of any column is zero. If H is a definite matrix, it can be made indefinite by adding two rows and columns such that the sum of the elements of each row and of each column becomes zero for each matrix H, Y, and Z. In this section, H will be considered as an indefinite matrix.

If the flow graph for Eqs. (3-33) is drawn with each equation taken in its normalized form, the normalized indefinite H flow graph is obtained. In this flow graph, the transmittances of all branches

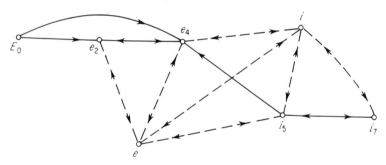

Fig. 3-17.   Indeterminate bidirectional graph of type H for the network of Fig. 3-13

which converge towards any node have the same denominator, which is the normalization factor. This normalization factor is equal to the nodal admittance if the node represents a voltage variable, or it is a mesh impedance if the node represents a current variable.

The indefinite bidirectional graph for the network of Fig. 3-13 can thus be obtained from the indefinite H matrix. This graph, which is shown in Fig. 3-17, makes use of voltage nodes for the subnetwork at the left and current nodes for the subnetwork at the right. The indefinite graph can of course be obtained from the definite graph already shown in Fig. 3-13c, by adding a node to each subgraph, and branches which join the interconnected nodes of the two graphs. These additional elements are shown as dotted lines in Fig. 3-17. The coefficients of the branches which join the two bidirectional sub-graphs are always ± 1. The sum of the coefficients of the branches which converge at or which diverge from any node is the immittance at that node; that is, it is a nodal admittance or a mesh impedance depending on whether the node represents a voltage or current.

The expansion rule can be applied to the hybrid bidirectional graphs as well as to the N or M type of graphs. For example, the transfer function for Fig. 3-13c or Fig. 3-17 is given by:

$$\frac{e_8}{E_0} = \frac{(Y_1 Y_3 + Y_9 Y_{22})Z_{75}Z_8}{\Delta} \tag{3-34}$$

with the determinant of the (definite) hybrid matrix given by Eq. (3-21):

$$\Delta = [Y_{22} Y_{44} - Y_3^2][Z_{55}Z_{77} - Z_{75}Z_{57}] + Y_{22}Z_{77} \tag{3-35}$$

It can be verified that the Eq. 3-34 is equal to the transfer function already obtained, as in Eq. (3-30), by applying Mason's rule to the flow graph.

4

Algebra of Quadripole and
N-port Networks Through
Signal Flow Graphs

4-1 INTRODUCTION

The application of matrix algebra to the study of electrical networks began around thirty years ago[31, 32]. Breisig[33] was the first
to use the term "quadripole" to characterize a network by giving
the relations between the input and output variables. The analysis
and synthesis of a network proceeded first by its decomposition into
two-port subnetworks which were themselves defined by the voltages
and currents at their terminals. By the use of matrix algebra, the
network could be represented by the interconnection of the quadripoles into which the network had previously been decomposed. The
quadripole algebra still remains a convenient method for the study
of certain problems. In this chapter, the algebra of quadripoles

will be developed with the help of signal flow graphs. By drawing these graphs in "quadripole form" one can establish the graph (that is the equations) of a network by interconnecting the elementary graphs in the same way that the subnetworks are interconnected. One advantage of this method is that the mathematical formulation of the problem remains much closer to the physical structure of the network with the use of flow graphs than with the use of the matrix equations. The flow graphs also increase the flexibility of this method of analysis of a network based on the decomposition into simpler interconnected structures. Effectively, with the matrix method, it is necessary that the matrices of the subnetworks be written in a particular form for a particular connection; this restriction almost disappears with the flow graph method. The calculations are simplified because of this and also because of the fact that the graphs can be evaluated by inspection with the use of Mason's rule.

Since the systematic organization of flow graphs permits the visualization of the relationships between the variables, it reveals itself as a fertile method. This is exemplified, in particular, in the section on ladder networks in which general formulas are developed for several types of ladder networks.

4-2 ALGEBRA OF QUADRIPOLE FLOW GRAPHS

4-2-1. Quadripole graphs. In order to specify an n-port network, it is necessary to write n equations relating $2n$ variables (voltages and currents at each port) in which half of the variables are independent and the others dependent. With all the possible choices of the independent set of variables, there will exist $(2n)! / (n!)^2$ possible types of different representations for this network. For a quadripole containing four variables, there are six types of equations which specify the relations between the voltages and currents of the input (e_1 and i_1) and the voltages and currents of the output (e_2 and i_2). These equations, given in flow graph form in Fig. 4-1, are characterized as being of type z or y or b, and so on, as indicated in brackets in the first column of the figure. In the case of the matrix or flow graph of type a, both the a_{ij} as well as the A, B, C, D parameters will be used since both of these are standard notation.

The flow graphs of Fig. 4-1 are the representation of the matrix equations given in the same figure. It is to be noted that the left-hand nodes correspond to the left-hand or input variables, and that

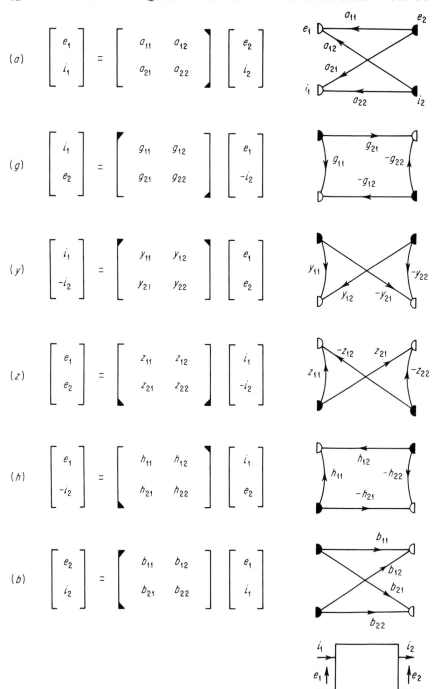

$(a)\quad \begin{bmatrix} e_1 \\ i_1 \end{bmatrix} = \begin{bmatrix} a_{11} & a_{12} \\ a_{21} & a_{22} \end{bmatrix} \begin{bmatrix} e_2 \\ i_2 \end{bmatrix}$

$(g)\quad \begin{bmatrix} i_1 \\ e_2 \end{bmatrix} = \begin{bmatrix} g_{11} & g_{12} \\ g_{21} & g_{22} \end{bmatrix} \begin{bmatrix} e_1 \\ -i_2 \end{bmatrix}$

$(y)\quad \begin{bmatrix} i_1 \\ -i_2 \end{bmatrix} = \begin{bmatrix} y_{11} & y_{12} \\ y_{21} & y_{22} \end{bmatrix} \begin{bmatrix} e_1 \\ e_2 \end{bmatrix}$

$(z)\quad \begin{bmatrix} e_1 \\ e_2 \end{bmatrix} = \begin{bmatrix} z_{11} & z_{12} \\ z_{21} & z_{22} \end{bmatrix} \begin{bmatrix} i_1 \\ -i_2 \end{bmatrix}$

$(h)\quad \begin{bmatrix} e_1 \\ -i_2 \end{bmatrix} = \begin{bmatrix} h_{11} & h_{12} \\ h_{21} & h_{22} \end{bmatrix} \begin{bmatrix} i_1 \\ e_2 \end{bmatrix}$

$(b)\quad \begin{bmatrix} e_2 \\ i_2 \end{bmatrix} = \begin{bmatrix} b_{11} & b_{12} \\ b_{21} & b_{22} \end{bmatrix} \begin{bmatrix} e_1 \\ i_1 \end{bmatrix}$

Fig. 4-1. Matrices and graphs for a two-port network

the right-hand nodes correspond to the right-hand or output variables, in order to maintain a correspondence between the ports of the network and the nodes of the flow graph. The voltage nodes will always be drawn in the top row and the current nodes in the bottom row of the graph.

In order to facilitate the interconnection of these graphs, it will be convenient to show explicitly the source and sink nodes. The source nodes will be drawn as black half-circles and the sink nodes as white half-circles. These flow graphs are in the form of quadripoles and are therefore called *quadripole flow graphs*. A particular graph will be called a graph of type z or y or b if it corresponds to a matrix of type z or y or b, respectively. It is to be noted that the output current i_2 is taken as flowing outward, that is to the right, in order to avoid changing signs when quadripoles are interconnected.

As an example, quadripole flow graphs for a simple series and shunt element have been given in Fig. 4-2. Columns (*b*) and (*d*) give the flow graphs in which only the terminal variables are indicated, whereas graphs of columns (*a*) and (*c*) are more detailed in that they show explicitly the voltage and current of the elements themselves. These latter variables are represented by the central nodes in the graph of columns (*a*) and (*c*). In these more detailed graphs, an impedance or an admittance term will appear no more than once. In degenerate cases of quadripoles, some of the six graphs might not exist. For example, in Fig. 4-2, the series impedance has no graph of type z and the shunt admittance has no graph of type y. Fig. 4-2 contains all possible representations of the series and shunt elements.

4-2-2. Interconnection of quadripole flow graphs. By considering a network as an interconnection of quadripoles, one will be able to represent this network by drawing suitable types of quadripole flow graphs, and by interconnecting these graphs in the same way as the quadripoles themselves are interconnected. This interconnection can be effected with the graphs either by superimposing the half-nodes of two different quadripole flow graphs or by bringing them together in order to complete the nodes. If a variable of the network is an independent variable for several quadripoles, it is necessary that it become a source half-node in the graph after the interconnection of the source half-nodes of the subgraphs. The same condition holds for the dependent variables. If, however, a variable

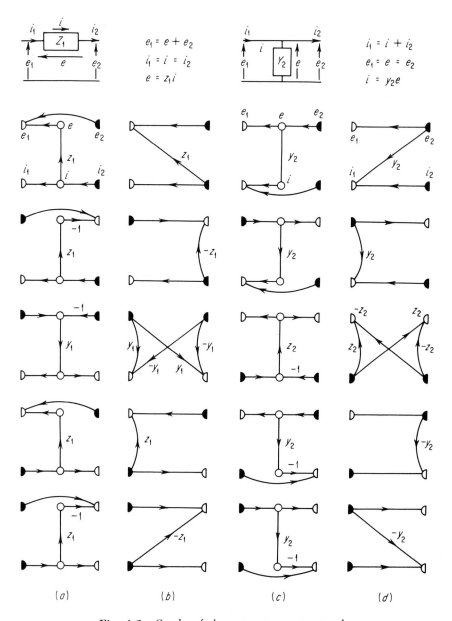

$$e_1 = e + e_2$$
$$i_1 = i = i_2$$
$$e = z_1 i$$

$$i_1 = i + i_2$$
$$e_1 = e = e_2$$
$$i = y_2 e$$

Fig. 4-2. Graphs of elementary two-port networks

is considered as independent for one quadripole and dependent for another quadripole connected to the first, the interconnection of the subgraphs will produce an internal node by the union of the source half-node and the sink half-node associated with that variable. With the convention already established for the source half-nodes (black) and the sink half-nodes (white), there is only one rule for the interconnection of the quadripole flow graphs:

"*all the half-nodes which are superimposed must be of the same type, and all the half-nodes connected together to complete a node must be of different types.*"

It is, of course, necessary to consider Kirchhoff's laws to decide which of the half-nodes must be superimposed and which must be connected together. The complete network is assembled from the quadripoles, and the interconnections can be performed one at a time at one port of a group of quadripoles. These interconnections are therefore either series or parallel.

In the parallel interconnection of n quadripoles, Kirchhoff's current law requires that:

$$i_j = \sum_{k=1}^{n} i_k \qquad (k \neq j) \qquad (4\text{-}1)$$

A complete node will therefore be formed with the current half-nodes, by joining together a source half-node (black) for i_j and a sink half-node. This sink half-node (white) is the superposition of the white half-node of all the quadripoles other than j. The dual situation applies for the voltages. It is necessary to superimpose $(n - 1)$ black half-nodes and to join the resultant half-node to the other (white) half-node, since the voltage at this terminal is defined by one of the quadripoles and is the same for all the others.

In the series connection of n quadripoles, the dual situation applies for the currents and voltages. Using the voltage law:

$$e_j = \sum_{k=1}^{n} e_k \qquad (k \neq j) \qquad (4\text{-}2)$$

a complete node is formed with a source half-node (e_j) and a sink half-node. This sink half-node will consist of the superposition of the white half-nodes of the other $(n - 1)$ quadripoles. One of the n current half-nodes defines the current for the other $n - 1$ quadripoles whose black current half-nodes are superimposed.

To simplify the drawing of the flow graph, to produce a neater picture, and to maintain a closer correspondence with the representation of the equations of the physical system being studied, the flow

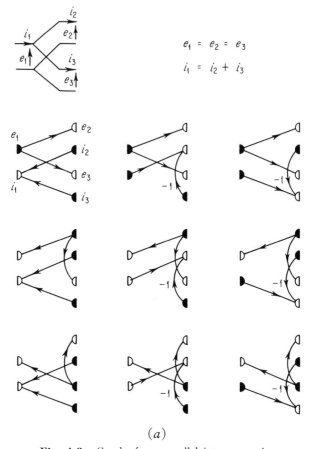

$$e_1 = e_2 = e_3$$

$$i_1 = i_2 + i_3$$

(a)

Fig. 4-3. Graphs for a parallel interconnection

graphs for the interconnections themselves will also be given. In this way, the subgraphs can first be drawn for each different quadripole and laid out in a disposition identical to the layout of the subnetworks themselves. The graphs for the interconnections are then drawn in order to complete the over-all flow graph. The transmittances which represent the flow graph of the interconnections are always equal to $+1$ or -1, and for simplicity the values of the transmittances equal to $+1$ will be omitted in the graph.

There are n^2 possible graphs to represent the interconnection of n terminal-pairs in series or in parallel. An example of a parallel and a series connection for three ports is given in Figs. 4-3a and 4-3b (dual to 4-3a). It is, of course, not necessary to draw all these graphs since a very simple inversion will produce one form from any

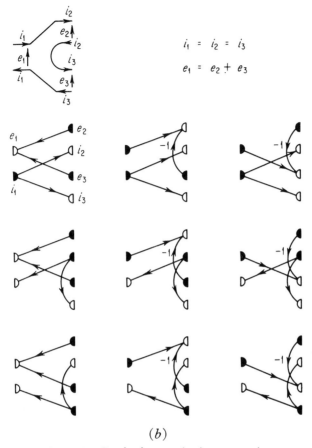

$$i_1 = i_2 = i_3$$

$$e_1 = e_2 + e_3$$

(b)

Fig. 4-3. Graphs for a series interconnection

other. For n terminal-pairs connected in parallel, one of the voltage half-nodes can be chosen as a source and one of the current half-nodes as a sink for the graphs representing the interconnection. In the same manner for the series connection, one of the current half-nodes can be chosen as source and one of the voltage half-nodes as sink.

The graph obtained by drawing the subgraphs of each quadripole and the subgraphs for the interconnections contain all of the current and voltage variables at each terminal-pair. Other graphs can be obtained for the same network by inversion of certain branches. Any of these graphs can be simplified by the reduction processes (Chapt. 1) to produce a residual graph which shows only the variables of interest.

4-3 APPLICATIONS

In order to illustrate the applications of the techniques described above, and to suggest other useful ones, a few specific examples will now be given.

4-3-1. Cascaded quadripoles. As an example of cascaded quadripoles, consider two quadripoles N_1 and N_2 connected as shown in

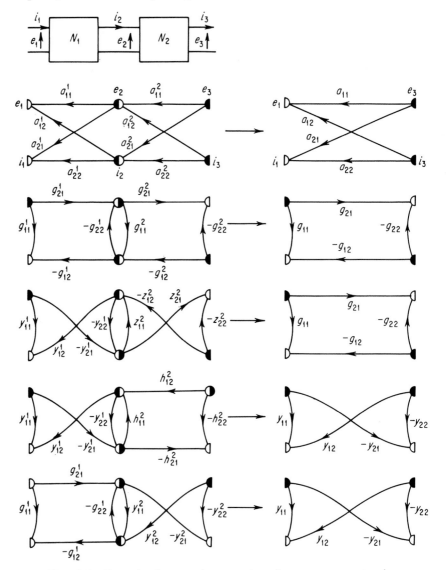

Fig. 4-4. Example of a cascade connection of two two-port networks

Fig. 4-4. One of the quadripoles can be represented by one of the six possible flow graphs of Fig. 4-1, and there remain one or two possible choices for the other quadripole. The interconnection is obtained by assembling the graphs in the order N_1-N_2, taking care that the half-nodes connected together are of opposite color. This automatically assures that the dependent variables of one graph become the independent variables for the other graph. The matrix method requires an inversion before multiplication if the matrices are not in the a form. For n cascaded quadripoles, the flow graphs allow $2(2^n + 1)$ possible choices, whereas the matrix method allows only one. Fig. 4-4 contains only five of the ten possible flow graphs. Each complete graph on the left (Fig. 4-4) is reduced to a resultant quadripole flow graph on the right. From these graphs, one can immediately "read" the quadripole coefficients of the complete network in terms of the characteristics of the individual quadripoles N_1 and N_2. For example, from the fourth graph in Fig. 4-4, the admittance parameters of the complete network can be obtained. These are:

$$y_{11} = y_{11}^1 - \frac{y_{21}^1 h_{11}^2 y_{12}^1}{D_{yh}}$$

$$y_{12} = \frac{y_{12}^1 h_{12}^2}{D_{yh}}$$

$$-y_{21} = \frac{y_{21}^1 h_{21}^2}{D_{yh}} \qquad (4\text{-}3)$$

$$-y_{22} = -h_{22}^2 + \frac{h_{12}^2 y_{22}^1 h_{21}^2}{D_{yh}}$$

$$D_{yh} = 1 + y_{22}^1 h_{11}^2$$

4-3-2. Interconnection of three quadripoles. The use of quadripole flow graphs allows a greater simplicity in the case where the interconnections are more complicated than simple cascaded structures. Consider, for example, a network formed by one quadripole N_1 cascaded with the parallel combination of two quadripoles N_2 and N_3. Three different graphs are shown in Fig. 4-5 and the corresponding reduced graphs in the right-hand column. It is not necessary to make further reductions of these graphs. For example, from the graph of Fig. 4-5d one obtains:

$$y_{11} = g_{11}^1 - \frac{g_{21}^1 y_{11}^{23} g_{12}^1}{D_3}$$

$$y_{12} = \frac{-g_{12}^1 y_{12}^{23}}{D_3}$$

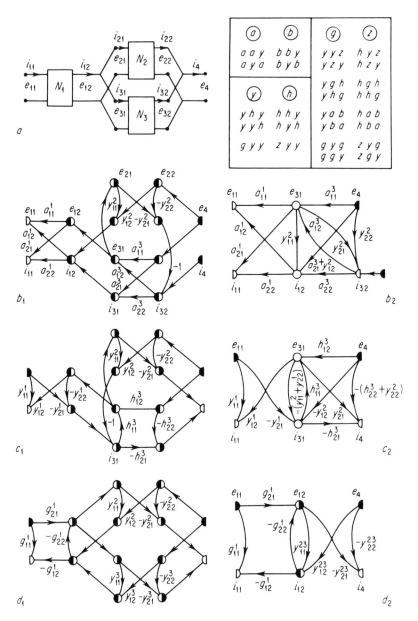

Fig. 4-5. Graphs for a network of three two-port networks

$$- y_{21} = \frac{- g_{21}^1 y_{21}^{23}}{D_3}$$

$$- y_{22} = - y_{22}^{23} + \frac{y_{12}^{23} g_{22}^1 y_{21}^{23}}{D_3}$$

where:
$$D_3 = 1 + g_{22}^1 y_{11}^{23}$$

$$y_{jk}^{23} = y_{jk}^2 + y_{jk}^3$$

The structure of the flow graph will depend on the form of matrices specified for N_1, N_2, and N_3 as well as on the type of graph desired for the over-all network. For this particular network, there are twenty-six possible forms of flow graph, three of which are shown in Fig. 4-5. Such flexibility in the choice of flow graph enables one to obtain the desired result by inspection, provided a convenient graph is first drawn out. It is therefore useful in these types of problems to have a feeling for the possible types of graphs and to choose that one which simplifies the algebra. The twenty-six possible forms of flow graphs are indicated in the table of Fig. 4-5. In this table, the encircled letter indicates the type of the over-all flow graph, and underneath are indicated the types of quadripole flow graphs (in the order N_1, N_2, and N_3) which will realize a resultant graph of the type specified.

4-3-3. Example of a more complex network. The rapidity and facility with which a flow graph can be obtained for a physical system is better illustrated in the following example. It is desired to analyze the network consisting of seven quadripoles shown in Fig. 4-6 in order to obtain the admittance matrix or flow graph for the complete network.

For this example, there are at least 381 different forms of flow graphs (159 of type z, 78 of type g, 55 of type h, 38 of type y, 26 of type a, and 25 of type b). Naturally, the complexity is not the same for each of these graphs and there is a choice to make in order to obtain the most suitable form.

For networks connected in *PP* (parallel-parallel), the y form of flow graph is the most natural form to use, whereas the forms g, h and z, are more convenient for *PS* (parallel-series), *SP* (series-parallel) and *SS* (series-series) connections, respectively. Therefore, in a network in which there are many parallel connections it will be logical to try to use as many y forms of flow graphs as possible and to complete the representation with those of type g and h. The combination y-z is to be avoided, in general, since when y and z forms

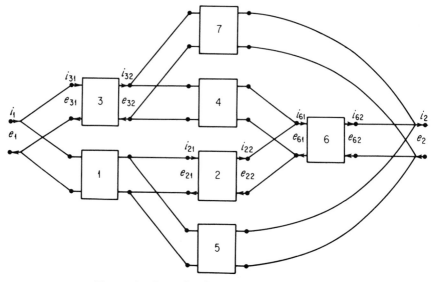

Fig. 4-6. Example of a more complex network

are used in the same graph, many loops are introduced. The same remark applies for the combinations of types *a* and *b* as well as that of *g* and *h*.

For the network of Fig. 4-6, graphs of type *y* will be used for the subnetworks N_7, N_4, N_2, and N_5 and also for the complete net-

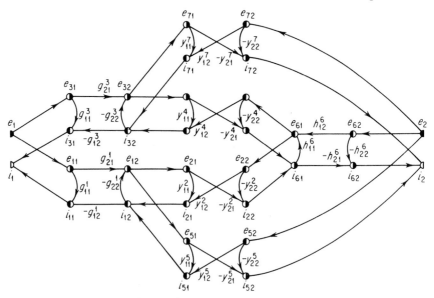

Fig. 4-7. A possible graph for the network of Fig. 4-6

work. The whole graph is thereby immediately characterized, since a g form must be used for N_3 and N_1, and an h form for N_6. The resulting flow graph is shown in Fig. 4-7, and with practice such a flow graph can be obtained easily and quickly. An immediate simplification is the absorption of the nodes associated with the quadri-

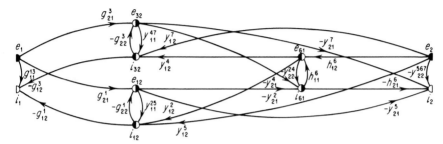

Fig. 4-8. Simplification of the graph of Fig. 4-7 with elementary transformations

$$g_{11}^{13} = g_{11}^1 + g_{11}^3 \qquad y_{22}^{567} = y_{22}^5 + h_{22}^6 + y_{22}^7$$

poles connected in parallel. From the resultant graph shown in Fig. 4-8, the admittance coefficients can be obtained by the use of Mason's rule. For example, the input admittance is given by:

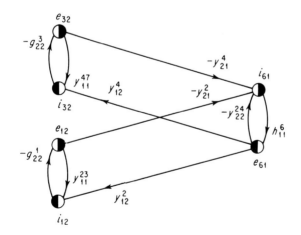

Fig. 4-9. Determinant of the graph of Fig. 4-8

$$D = 1 + (g_{22}^3 y_{11}^{47} + g_{22}^1 h_{11}^{25} + y_{22}^{24} h_{11}^6 - g_{22}^3 y_{21}^4 - g_{22}^1 y_{21}^2 h_{11}^6 y_{12}^2)$$
$$+ (g_{22}^3 y_{11}^{47})(g_{22}^1 y_{11}^{25}) + (g_{22}^3 y_{11}^{47})(y_{22}^{24} h_{11}^6) + (g_{22}^1 y_{11}^{25})(y_{22}^{24} h_{11}^6)$$
$$- (g_{22}^3 y_{11}^{47})(g_{22}^1 y_{21}^2 h_{11}^6 y_{12}^2) - (g_{22}^1 y_{11}^{25})(g_{22}^3 y_{21}^4 h_{11}^6 y_{12}^4)$$
$$+ (g_{11}^3 y_{11}^{47})(g_{22}^1 y_{11}^{25})(y_{22}^2 h_{11}^6)$$
$$D_1 = 1 + (g_{22}^3 y_{11}^{47} + y_{22}^{24} h_{11}^6 - g_{22}^3 y_{21}^4 h_{11}^6 y_{12}^4) + (g_{22}^3 y_{11}^{47})(y_{22}^{24} h_{11}^6)$$
$$D_3 = 1 + (g_{22}^1 y_{11}^{25} + y_{22}^{24} h_{11}^6 - g_{22}^1 y_{21}^2 h_{11}^6 y_{12}^2) + (g_{22}^1 y_{11}^{25})(y_{22}^{24} h_{11}^6)$$

$$y_{11} = g_{11}^{13} + \frac{g_{21}^{3}}{D}\left\{y_{21}^4 h_{11}^6[y_{12}^4 g_{12}^3(1 + g_{22}^1 y_{11}^{25}) + y_{12}^2 g_{12}^1] - y_{11}^{47} g_{12}^3 D_3\right\}$$

$$+ \frac{g_{21}^{1}}{D}\left\{-y_{11}^{25} g_{12}^4 D_1 + y_{21}^2 h_{11}^6[y_{12}^2 g_{12}^1(1 + g_{22}^3 y_{11}^{47}) + y_{12}^4 g_{12}^3]\right\} \quad (4\text{-}5)$$

D is the graph determinant which can be computed from a new residual graph (Fig. 4-9) obtained by removing the source and sink nodes. The minors D_1 and D_3 can also be obtained directly from the flow graph.

4-3-4. Flow graph quadripoles with sources. Active networks are usually analyzed by starting from equivalent circuits containing, in addition to the passive elements, sources which depend on voltages or currents in the network. The flow graphs for these circuits are easily obtained by drawing quadripole flow graphs for the passive elements and then superimposing on them additional branches which represent the dependent sources. It remains well understood, of course, that here again desired operations such as inversions and reductions can still be performed.

Fig. 4-10 gives one form of flow graph for an elementary quadripole consisting of a series or shunt element with a current or voltage source. Other forms can be obtained by inversions performed on these graphs.

In this manner, the y type of flow graph, for example, can be assembled for a triode with a grounded cathode (Fig. 4-11) or with a grounded grid (Fig. 4-12).

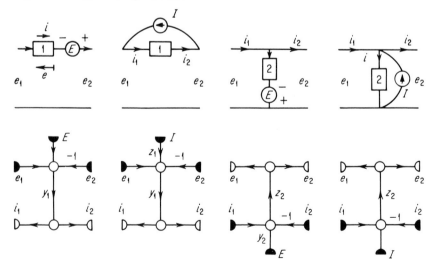

Fig. 4-10. Shunt or series elements with sources

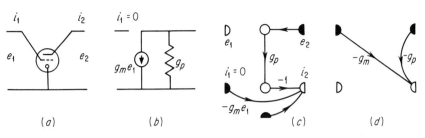

Fig. 4-11. Grounded cathode triode

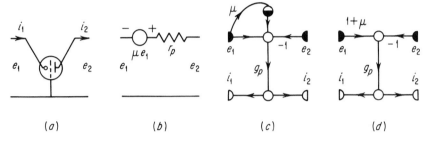

Fig. 4-12. Grounded grid triode

Since the relations between the variables at the terminals of the quadripole are used, it is also possible to consider networks having distributed parameters. Thus, one equivalent circuit for the transistor[34] of Fig. 4-13a consisting of transmission lines N_1 and N_2 and dependent sources, in series with an impedance Z_b, can be represented immediately by the flow graph of Fig. 4-13b. The over-all flow graph has been drawn in a z form in order to obtain directly the open circuit impedances:

$$z_{11} = z_b + h_{11}^1 / D$$

$$z_{12} = z_b + g_{22}^2 \mu h_{12}^1 / D$$

$$z_{21} = z_b + h_{11}^1 g_{21}^2 / \mu D$$

$$z_{22} = z_b + g_{22}^2 / D$$

$$D = 1 - h_{12}^1 g_{21}^2$$

4-3-5. Operational amplifiers. The analysis of operational units for an analog computer consisting of an amplifier and of a more or less complex network constitutes an interesting application of the method described in the present chapter. For the network of Fig. 4-14, subgraphs of type a will be chosen for the subnetworks N_6, N_3, and the amplifier, which are connected in cascade, and graphs of type y for the quadripoles N_5 and N_2 which are connected in parallel with the rest of the network. The resultant graph as well as a residual

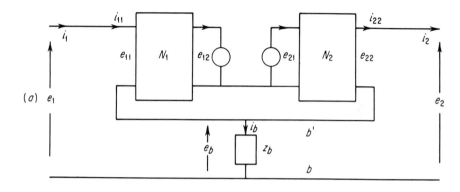

$$e_{12} = \mu e_{22} \; ; \; e_{21} = e_{11}/\mu$$

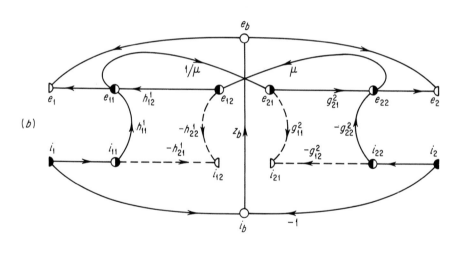

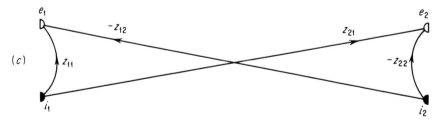

Fig. 4-13. Flow graph for a transistor

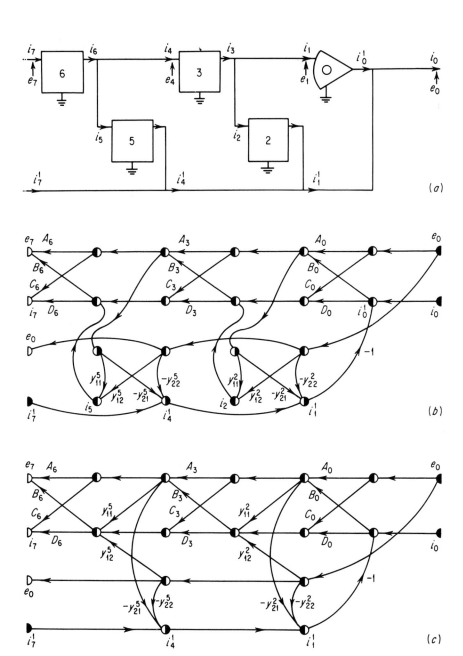

Fig. 4-14. Flow graph of a general operational amplifier

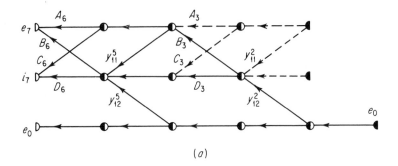

$$\begin{bmatrix} e_7 \\ i_7 \\ e_0 \end{bmatrix} = \begin{bmatrix} A_6 & B_6 & 0 \\ C_6 & D_6 & 0 \\ 0 & 0 & 1 \end{bmatrix} \begin{bmatrix} 1 & 0 & 0 \\ y_{11}^5 & 1 & y_{12}^5 \\ 0 & 0 & 1 \end{bmatrix} \begin{bmatrix} A_3 & B_3 & 0 \\ C_3 & D_3 & 0 \\ 0 & 0 & 1 \end{bmatrix} \begin{bmatrix} 1 & 0 & 0 \\ y_{11}^2 & 1 & y_{12}^2 \\ 0 & 0 & 1 \end{bmatrix} \begin{bmatrix} 0 \\ 0 \\ e_0 \end{bmatrix}$$

(*b*)

$$\begin{bmatrix} e_7 \\ i_7 \\ e_0 \end{bmatrix} = \begin{bmatrix} A_6 + B\,y_{11}^5 & B_6 & B_6\,y_{12}^5 \\ C_6 + D_6\,y_{11}^5 & D_6 & D_6\,y_{12}^5 \\ 0 & 0 & 1 \end{bmatrix} \begin{bmatrix} A_3 + B_3\,y_{11}^2 & B_3 & B_3\,y_{12}^2 \\ C_3 + D_3\,y_{11}^2 & D_3 & D_3\,y_{12}^2 \\ 0 & 0 & 1 \end{bmatrix} \begin{bmatrix} 0 \\ 0 \\ e_0 \end{bmatrix}$$

(*c*)

Fig. 4-15. Graph for a high gain amplifier and matrix factorization derived from the flow graph

graph are given in Fig. 4-14. In the particularly interesting case of a high-gain amplifier with infinite input impedance ($e_1 = i_1 = 0$), the coefficients for the cascade matrix of the amplifier are zero and the graph of Fig. 4-15 is therefore obtained. This cascade graph gives immediately the voltage transfer function:

$$e_7 / e_0 = (A_6 + B_6 Y_{11}^5)B_3 Y_{12}^2 + (D_3 Y_{12}^2 + y_{12}^5)B_6 \qquad (4\text{-}6)$$

It is possible, if desired, to obtain matrix factorizations from the cascade graph as indicated in Fig. 4-15. One can group the sections of the cascade graph as desired and the chain matrix of order three for the complete network is the product of the chain matrices of each section considered.

Eq. 4-6 permits writing the transfer function for the particular case where the quadripoles are in the form of T networks, as indicated in Fig. 4-16.

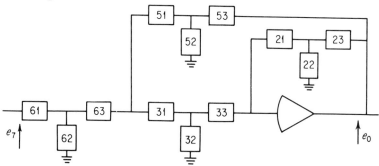

Fig. 4-16. Example of operational amplifier

$$\frac{e_0}{e_7} = -\frac{(Z_{21} + Z_{23} + Z_{21}Y_{22}Z_{23})(Z_{51} + Z_{53} + Z_{51}Y_{52}Z_{53})}{D}$$

$$D = (Z_{31} + Z_{33} + Z_{31}Y_{32}Z_{33})[(1 + Z_{61}Y_{62})(Z_{51} + Z_{53} + Z_{51}Y_{52}Z_{53})$$
$$+ (1 + Y_{52}Z_{53})(Z_{61} + Z_{63} + Z_{61}Y_{62}Z_{63})]$$
$$+ (Z_{61} + Z_{63} + Z_{61}Y_{62}Z_{63})[(1 + Y_{32}Z_{33})(Z_{51} + Z_{53} + Z_{51}Y_{52}Z_{53})$$
$$+ (Z_{21} + Z_{23} + Z_{21}Y_{22}Z_{23})]$$

4-4 APPLICATIONS TO LADDER NETWORKS

Ladder networks are of special interest in the study of filters and in problems of synthesis in general. This comes from the fact that the admittance and impedance matrices for these networks have a particularly simple structure, with nonzero elements only on the principal diagonal and on the adjacent diagonals. This simplicity will also be found in the flow graphs. The flow graphs of type a in particular contain no loops but are only cascade graphs; they correspond to chain matrices which can be multiplied directly to obtain the matrix of the whole network. The flow graph permits a systematization of the calculation of the parameters of this matrix, such that it becomes unnecessary to draw the graph. In this section, several well-known results will be obtained in a simple and elegant manner with the help of the a type of flow graphs. Furthermore, to illustrate how the flow graphs can help to organize the algebra and to suggest a systematization of the properties of a given network, the equations of tapered ladder networks will be established in an original manner.

4-4-1. Calculation of the parameters of the chain matrix. A ladder network will be represented schematically as in Fig. 4-17 by numbering the elements from left to right. Odd number indices will be used for the series elements which will be defined by their impedances Z_1, Z_3, ... and even numbered indices will be used for the shunt elements defined by their admittances Y_2, Y_4, ... It is convenient to use graphs of type *a*, as shown in Fig. 4-17. The transmittances not specifically indicated in the graph are equal to 1. The graphs thus obtained are cascade graphs which can be evaluated by summation of the transmittances of all the open paths between a source and a sink node.

With the notation already introduced to designate the branches of the ladder network, the open paths are direct paths as defined in the first chapter. Also, it will always be possible to write the factors of each term of a response in such a way that the indices are successively increasing. To simplify the writing of the expressions, the terms will be represented by their indices indicated in parenthesis in the following manner:

$$ZY(12, 14, ...) = Z_1 Y_2 + Z_1 Y_4 + ... \qquad (4-7)$$

For example, for a ladder of six elements for which the flow graph is given in Fig. 4-17, the first term of the cascade matrix is:

$$A_6 = 1 + ZY(12, 14, 16, 34, 36, 56)$$
$$+ ZYZY(1234, 1236, 1256, 1456, 3456) + ZYZYZY(123456)$$

It can also be verified that the coefficient C is given by the following expression:

$$C_6 = Y(2, 4, 6) + YZY(234, 236, 256, 456) + YZYZY(23456)$$

The law of formation of the expression of any term can be resumed as follows:

1. the sum is taken on all terms of the same order such that the indices alternate between odd and even numbers and also increase successively for each factor of the same term.

2. each term is of order greater than the previous one by a factor ZY or YZ.

Thus, for the ladder network in which the elements are numbered as in Fig. 4-17, and where the number of elements is either $2n$, $2n - 1$, or $2n + 1$ depending on the case, the following expressions are obtained:

$$A_{2n} = A_{2n+1} = 1 + \sum Z_{j1} Y_{k2} + \sum Z_{j1} Y_{k2} Z_{j3} Y_{k4} ...$$

$$B_{2n-1} = B_{2n} = \sum Z_{j1} + \sum Z_{j1}Y_{k2}Z_{j3} + \sum Z_{j1}Y_{k2}Z_{j3}Y_{k4}Z_{j5} \ldots \quad (4\text{-}8)$$

$$C_{2n} = C_{2n+1} = \sum Y_{k2} + \sum Y_{k2}Z_{j3}Y_{k4} + \sum Y_{k2}Z_{j3}Y_{k4}Z_{j5}Y_{k6} \ldots$$

$$D_{2n-1} = D_{2n} = 1 + \sum Y_{k2}Z_{j3} + \sum Y_{k2}Z_{j3}Y_{k4}Z_{j5} \ldots$$

The summation is done for all possible values of the odd indices:

$$j_1, j_3, j_5 \ldots j_{2n-1} = 1, 3, 5 \ldots 2n - 1$$

and for all possible values of the even indices:

$$k_2, k_4, k_6 \ldots k_{2n} = 2, 4, 6, \ldots 2n$$

with the restriction that successive indices of the same term form an increasing sequence:

$$j_1 < k_2 < j_3 < k_4 \ldots < j_{2n-1} < k_{2n}$$

the maximum index being less than or equal to the number of elements of the network.

The number of terms of each sum is given by Pascal's triangle. This triangle appears in Fig. 4-17b. The integers in the triangle are written at the intersection of two lines which are projected outside of the triangle. These lines indicate respectively the coefficient (with subscript j) of the cascade matrix for the ladder network (consisting of j elements), and also the order of the term which it is desired to consider (1 or ZY or ZYZ, and so on). The number of these terms is read at the intersection of the two lines. Thus, for a ladder of seven elements, it can be verified that the coefficient A_7 ($= A_6$) contains five terms of order four of form $ZYZY$.

4-4-2. Geometrically tapered ladder networks. The calculation of the parameters of the cascade matrix will be applied in this section to a particular class of ladder networks in which there is a constant ratio between the value of the series elements, as well as between the values of the shunt elements.

1. Binary representation of the terms of an expression of the A, B, C, D parameters. To obtain a simple expression for the parameters of the cascade matrix of ladder networks considered in this section, it is convenient first to establish an analytical representation of the open paths of the flow graph of Fig. 4-17. Since the parameters of the elements appear only once in the graph, any path from source to sink can be represented by a "binary word" which has as many bits as there are elements in the graph. The position of each bit corresponds to the index of an element of the network, and this bit will be 1 or 0 depending on whether or not the element appears in the path considered. For example, in a network of twelve elements, one term of A

has the form $Z_3 Y_6 Z_7 Y_8$; its binary representation will be 001001110000. The branches having unit transmittances will, of course, not appear in this binary representation. If these bits are taken as the exponents of the impedances or admittances (written from left to right in increasing order of the indices), a mathematical expression is obtained

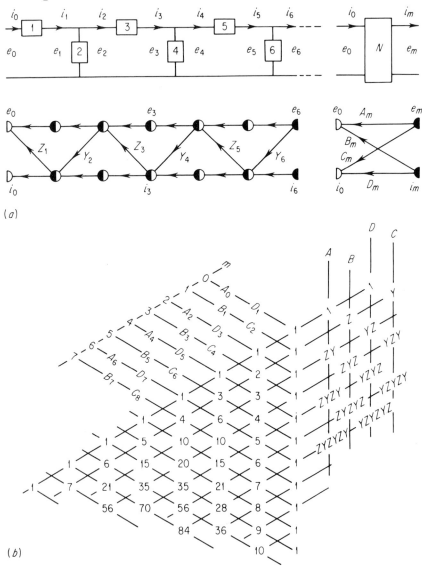

(a)

(b)

Fig. 4-17. Graph of type a for a ladder network and Pascal's triangle to compute the number of terms in the expansion of the chain matrix

for a path transmittance. Thus, the path considered above can be expressed as:

$$Z_3 Y_6 Z_7 Y_8 = Z_1^0 Y_2^0 Z_3^1 Y_4^0 Z_5^0 Y_6^1 Z_7^1 Y_8^1 Z_9^0 Y_{10}^0 Z_{11}^0 Y_{12}^0$$

Consider the network of Fig. 4-17a with elements $Z_1 Y_2 Z_3 Y_4 \ldots Y_{2n}$. The general form of the binary expression for a path will be $a_1 b_2 a_3 b_4 \ldots b_{2n}$, where the binary characters a and b correspond to Z and Y, respectively. In order for a binary word to represent the transmittance of any path, it must satisfy the following conditions (which can be verified by inspection of the flow graph). 1. There must be an even number of zeros between any two nonzero bits. 2. The terms of the coefficients A and D are represented by binary words having an even number $(0, 2, 4, \ldots)$ of ones, whereas those of B and C contain an odd number of ones. The number of ones will be designated by p. This number is the order of the terms considered in the expressions of the A, B, C, D. The maximum order will be designated by m. 3. The first and last ones of the binary word for the A, B, C and D are a and b, a and a, b and b, and b and a, respectively.

With these restrictions, a general formula can be written for any a_{ij} (A, B, C or D) of the cascade matrix for a ladder network having $2n$ elements:

$$a_{ij} = \sum Z_1^{a_1} Y_2^{b_2} Z_3^{a_3} Y_4^{b_4} \ldots Y_{2n}^{b_{2n}} \qquad (4\text{-}9)$$

For a ladder in which the series element Z_1 or the shunt one Y_{2n} (or both) are zero, it is only necessary to remove the corresponding factors in Eq. (4-9).

It is convenient to represent all the binary words of a coefficient a_{ij} in a table as in the example of Fig. 4-18 for a ladder of six elements $Z_1, Y_2 \ldots Y_6$. The order p of the terms has been indicated in the left-hand column.

For any coefficient a_{ij}, the number of terms of order p in the Eq. (4-9) depends on p and m only. Since the zeros appear in pairs, there will therefore be $(m - p)/2$ pairs of zeros. There are p ones in the binary word for a term of order p. The number of terms will therefore be the combination of $p + (m - p)/2$ objects taken p at a time, that is:

$$N = \begin{pmatrix} \dfrac{m+p}{2} \\ p \end{pmatrix} = \begin{pmatrix} \dfrac{m+p}{2} \\ \dfrac{m-p}{2} \end{pmatrix}$$

A_6							B_6					
p	a_1	b_2	a_3	b_4	a_5	b_6	p	a_1	b_2	a_3	b_4	a_5	b_6
0	0	0	0	0	0	0	1	1	0	0	0	0	0
2	1	1	0	0	0	0		0	0	1	0	0	0
	1	0	0	1	0	0		0	0	0	0	1	0
	1	0	0	0	0	1	3	1	1	1	0	0	0
	0	0	1	1	0	0		1	1	0	0	1	0
	0	0	1	0	0	1		1	0	0	1	1	0
	0	0	0	0	1	1		0	0	1	1	1	0
4	1	1	1	1	0	0	5	1	1	1	1	1	0
	1	1	1	0	0	1							
	1	1	0	0	1	1							
	1	0	0	1	1	1							
	0	0	1	1	1	1							

C_6						
p	a_1	b_2	a_3	b_4	a_5	b_6
1	0	1	0	0	0	0
	0	0	0	1	0	0
	0	0	0	0	0	1
3	0	1	1	1	0	0
	0	1	1	0	0	1
	0	1	0	0	1	1
	0	0	0	1	1	1
5	0	1	1	1	1	1

A6 table continued:

p	a_1	b_2	a_3	b_4	a_5	b_6
6	1	1	1	1	1	1

D_6						
p	a_1	b_2	a_3	b_4	a_5	b_6
0	0	0	0	0	0	0
2	0	1	1	0	0	0
	0	1	0	0	1	0
	0	0	0	1	1	0
4	0	1	1	1	1	0

Fig. 4-18. Binary representation of the open paths of the graph of Fig. 4-17

These values of N are the numbers appearing in Pascal's triangle of Fig. 4-17b along the lines indicated by the value of m.

2. *Expressions for the coefficients of the chain matrix.* The double tapered ladder networks to be studied in this section consist of series impedances $Z_1, Z_3 = rZ_1, \ldots Z_{2n+1} = r^n Z_1$ and shunt admittances $Y_2, Y_4 = gY_2, \ldots Y_{2n+2} = g^n Y_2$. The product $Z_1 Y_2$ will be designated by h, which in general depends on frequency.

For these networks, each term of Eq. (4-8) can be expressed as a function of Z_1, Y_2 and of a factor $r^\alpha g^\beta$ where

$$\alpha = \sum n a_{2n+1}$$
$$\beta = \sum n b_{2n+2} \qquad (n = 0, 1, 2, \ldots)$$

This pair α, β, can be obtained by grouping the pairs a, b, of a binary word and by multiplying each pair by $0, 1, 2, \ldots$ respectively, according to their position in the binary word and then summing. An α, β, pair can thus be calculated for each binary word after having tabulated these words as in the example of Fig. 4-18.

A set $\{\alpha, \beta\}$ can be defined as consisting of the pairs α, β, calculated from a table of binary words which have been grouped by values of p. Any subset of α, β, which is contained at the end of one group and at the beginning of the next group, in two groups corresponding to successively higher values of p, will be written only once. For example, the set $\{\alpha, \beta\}$ for the coefficient A_6 of Fig. 4-18 is:

$$\{\alpha, \beta\} = \{00 \quad 01 \quad 02 \quad 11 \quad 12 \quad 22 \quad 23 \quad 33\} \qquad (4\text{-}10)$$

A column matrix $P(rg)$ is defined as the matrix of the elements $r^\alpha g^\beta$ for the values of the set $\{\alpha, \beta\}$. For the example given above, one obtains $P_6(rg)$ whose transpose is:

$$P_6^t(rg) = (r^0 g^0 \quad r^0 g^1 \quad r^0 g^2 \quad r^1 g^1 \quad r^1 g^2 \quad r^2 g^2 \quad r^2 g^3 \quad r^3 g^3) \qquad (4\text{-}11)$$

The factors $Z_1 Y_2$ of Eq. (4-9) will appear as powers of $h = Z_1 Y_2$ or of rh. It is therefore convenient to define row matrices $[h]_n$ and $[rh]_n$ as:

$$[h]_n = (1 \quad h \quad h^2 \quad \ldots \quad h^n) \qquad (4\text{-}12)$$
$$[rh]_n = (1 \quad rh \quad r^2 h^2 \quad \ldots \quad r^n h^n) \qquad (4\text{-}13)$$

The matrices $P(rg)$ and $[h]$ contain all the factors of the different terms of Eq. (4-9). All of the terms of any coefficient a_{ij} can now be represented as the product of these types of matrices. These terms correspond to open paths of the graph; it is thus only necessary to enumerate these paths in an appropriate manner in a matrix L to obtain any coefficient a_{ij} in the form of the product of three matrices:

$$A_{2n} = A_{2n+1} = [h]_n L_{2n} P_{2n}(rg)$$
$$B_{2n-1} = B_{2n} = Z_1 [h]_{n-1} L_{2n-1} P_{2n-1}(gr)$$
$$C_{2n} = C_{n+1} = Y_2 [rh]_{n-1} L_{2n-1} P_{2n-1}(rg) \qquad (4\text{-}14)$$
$$D_{2n-1} = D_{2n} = [rh]_{n-2} L_{2n-2} P_{2n-2}(gr)$$

In these expressions, the matrix L is a rectangular matrix containing only ones (1) and zeros (0), and its rows correspond to successive values of p. Each row contains as many ones in succession as there exist open paths for the order corresponding to that row. Let the i'th integer of the m'th diagonal of the triangle of Fig. 4-17 be defined as $I(m, i)$; this integer gives the number of one's in the i'th row of L_m. The first 1 of row i is displaced to the left, relative to the first 1 of row $(i + 1)$ by a number of positions equal to the integer found directly above the integer $I(m, i)$ in the triangle. The matrix L_m contains as many rows as there are terms in the m'th diagonal of the triangle and a number of columns equal to the sum of the terms in the $(m - 1)'$th diagonal. These sums are Fibonacci numbers.

For example, for the ladder containing six elements (Fig. 4-18) the matrix L_6 becomes:

$$L_6 = \begin{vmatrix} 1 & & & & & & & \\ 1 & 1 & 1 & 1 & 1 & 1 & & \\ & & 1 & 1 & 1 & 1 & 1 & \\ & & & & & & & 1 \end{vmatrix} \qquad (4\text{-}15)$$

and the coefficient A_6 is expressed as:

$$A_6 = [h]_3 L_6 P_6(rg)$$
$$A_6 = 1 + h(1 + g + g^2 + rg + rg^2 + r^2g^2)$$
$$+ h^2(rg + rg^2 + r^2g^2 + r^2g^3 + r^3g^3) + h^3(r^3g^3)$$

A particular case of the preceding network is obtained when rg is made equal to 1. This represents a single-tapered ladder network in which the sections are identical except for a progressive change of impedance level from section to section. If $rg = 1$ is substituted in the matrix $P(rg)$, there will remain only powers of r or of g. It is therefore convenient to consider the set $\{|\alpha - \beta|\}$. For example, starting from Eq. (4-10), one obtains for the coefficient A_6:

$$\{|\alpha - \beta|\} = \{0 \quad 1 \quad 2 \quad 0 \quad 1 \quad 0 \quad 1 \quad 0\} \qquad (4\text{-}16)$$

The matrices L and P of Eq. (4-14) can therefore be simplified by writing:

L': obtained from L by adding together those columns which correspond to the same values in the set $\{|\alpha - \beta|\}$.

$[r]$ or $[g]$ matrices of the same form as the matrix of Eq. (4-12). Equations 4-14 therefore reduce to the form:

$$A_{2n} = A_{2n+1} = [h]_n L'_{2n} [g]^t_{n-1}$$
$$B_{2n-1} = B_{2n} = r^{n-1} Z_1 [h]_{n-1} L'_{2n-1} [g]^t_{n-1}$$
$$C_{2n} = C_{2n+1} = g^{n-1} Y_2 [rh]_{n-1} L'_{2n-1} [r]^t_{n-1} \tag{4-17}$$
$$D_{2n-1} = D_{2n} = [rh]_{n-1} L'_{2n-2} [r]^t_{n-2}$$

The coefficient A_6 for a network where $rg = 1$ can thus be expressed as:

$$A_6 = [1 \quad h \quad h^2 \quad h^3] \begin{bmatrix} 1 & & & \\ 3 & 2 & 1 & \\ 3 & 2 & & \\ 1 & & & \end{bmatrix} \begin{bmatrix} 1 \\ g \\ g^2 \end{bmatrix}$$

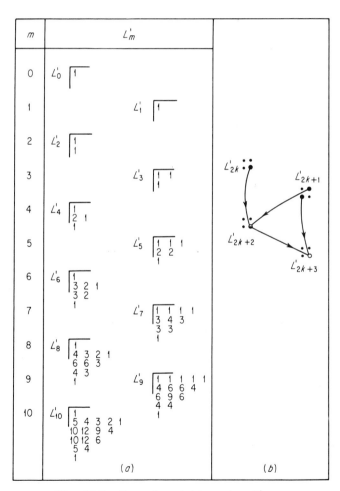

Fig. 4-19. Formation of the matrices L'_m

If, furthermore, $r = g = 1$, the matrices $[r]$ and $[g]$ contain only ones, and their product with L'_m gives a column matrix L''_m in which the elements are the integers of the m'th diagonal of Pascal's triangle of Fig. 4-17b. Equations 4-17 can therefore be reduced to the following expressions:

$$
\begin{aligned}
A_{2n} &= A_{2n+1} = [h]_n L''_{2n} = (-1)^n S_{2n}(-\sqrt{h}) \\
B_{2n-1} &= B_{2n} = Z_1 [h]_{n-1} L''_{2n-1} = (-1)^{n-1} Z_1 S_{2n-1}(-\sqrt{h}) \\
C_{2n} &= C_{2n+1} = Y_2 [h]_{n-1} L''_{2n-1} = (-1)^{n-1} Y_2 S_{2n-1}(-\sqrt{h}) \\
D_{2n-1} &= D_{2n} = [h]_{n-1} L''_{2n-2} = (-1)^{n-2} S_{2n-2}(-\sqrt{h})
\end{aligned}
\tag{4-18}
$$

where the S_{2n} are the Tschebyscheff polynomials. These results agree with those already appearing in the literature[35]. For the coefficient A_6 of a ladder network containing three identical sections with $Z_1 Y_2 = h$, one obtains:

$$
A_6 = 1 + 6h + 5h^2 + h^3
$$

Recurrence formulas can be obtained for the matrices L'_m. These matrices are given in the table of Fig. 4-19. Instead of giving the recurrence formula, a *"template flow graph"* has been drawn in this figure. This graph is a flow graph which represents the recurrence relations and is drawn on a separate sheet with a hole for each node. These holes must be placed in such a manner as to correspond to the positions into which the elements of L'_m are to be written on another sheet. The template is moved over the other sheet and the values which appear in the holes of the source nodes permit calculating the values which are to be written in the free holes.

4-4-3. Some matrix factorizations. Matrix factorization techniques, in which a matrix is decomposed into the product of several matrices, have been used for the synthesis of transfer functions. Two examples of matrix factorizations which have already been used for the synthesis of a network in the form of a ladder will be presented here through signal flow graphs. The flow graphs allow an easy visualization of the important relations and also a simplification of the algebra.

In a method described by Pantell[36], the elements of the ladder network are directly related to factors of the desired transfer function. It makes use of the simple L sections shown in the flow graph of Fig. 4-20a in which the transmittance a_{11} is null for $Z_2 Y_2 = 1$ and those of Fig. 4-20b in which a_{22} is null for $Y_3 Z_3 = 1$. If these simple sections are used in a ladder network (Fig. 4-20c), the graph

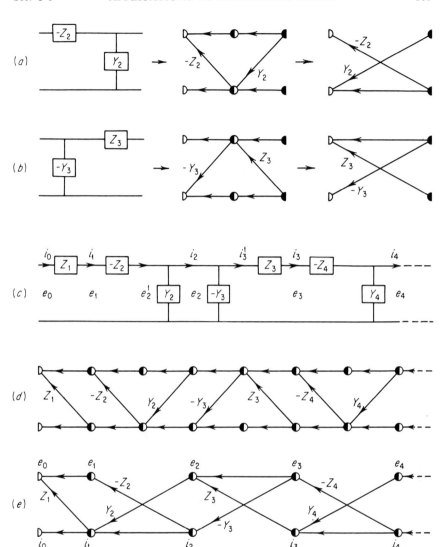

Fig. 4-20. Ladder network for the synthesis of transfer functions

of Fig. 4-20d is obtained which in turn is immediately reduced to the flow graph of Fig. 4-20e. This graph leads directly to the voltage transfer ratio for a ladder network with $2n$ elements. This transfer function is the inverse of the transmittance of the open path from source to sink:

$$T = \frac{e_{2n}}{e_0} = \frac{1}{Z_1} \frac{1}{Y_2} \frac{1}{Z_3} \frac{1}{Y_4} \cdots \frac{1}{Y_{2n}}$$

If the required transfer function is decomposed into factors:

$$T = KH(s) = \Pi k_i H_i(s)$$

where K and k_i are constants and $H(s)$ and $H_i(s)$ are functions of the frequency s, one obtains:

$$\frac{1}{Z_i} = k_i H_i(s); \quad i \text{ odd}$$

$$\frac{1}{Y_i} = k_i H_i(s); \quad i \text{ even}$$

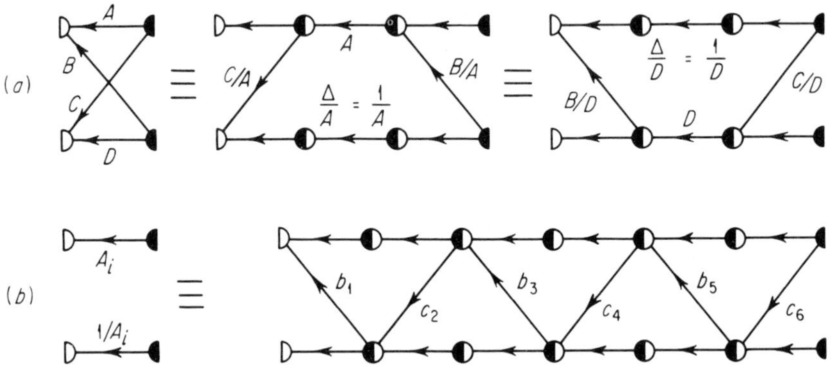

(n, m, k)	(n, m, k)	(n, m, k)	$(\frac{1}{A_i}, 1, k)$	$(A_i, 1, 1)$
b_1	k	$(n-1)k$	k	$A_i - 1$
c_2	$\dfrac{(n-1)}{k}$	$\dfrac{1}{k}$	$\dfrac{1-A_i}{kA_i}$	1
b_3	$\dfrac{(m-A_i)k}{(n-1)A_i}$	$\dfrac{(m-A_i)k}{A_i}$	k	$\dfrac{1-A_i}{A_i}$
c_4	$\dfrac{(n-1)(n-A_i)A_i}{k(A_i-mn)}$	$\dfrac{(n-A_i)A_i}{(A_i-mn)k}$	$\dfrac{(A_i-1)}{k}$	$-A_i$
b_5	$\dfrac{(A_i-mn)k}{A_i^2(n-1)}$	$\dfrac{(A_i-mn)k}{A_i^2}$	$\dfrac{(A+1)k}{A_i^2}$	0
c_6	$\dfrac{(n-1)(m-1)A_i^2}{k(A_i-mn)}$	$\dfrac{(m-1)A_i^2}{(A_i-mn)k}$	0	0

Fig. 4-21. Expansion of a ladder network from its chain matrix

It will be sufficient to take each $H_i(s)$ as a realizable driving point function and to choose the k_i such that the series impedances

$$Z_{2i+1} - Z_{2i+2}$$

and the shunt admittances

$$Y_{2i} - Y_{2i+1}$$

are realizable driving point functions.

The flow graph suggests other possible extensions of this method by the use of other parameters of the matrix for the synthesis of other transfer functions.

Another factorization of the chain matrix is indicated in Fig. 4-21a for a passive reciprocal quadripole $(AD - BC = 1)$. The central section of this graph can be decomposed into several factors and each of these can be realized as a ladder element as suggested by Fig. 4-21b. In effect, it suffices to make certain that the following equations (in case of a ladder of six elements) are satisfied:

$$A_i = 1 + bc(12, 14, 16, 34, 36, 56)$$
$$+ \, bcbc(1234, 1236, 1256, 1456, 3456) + bcbcbc(123456)$$

$$B_i = 0 = b(1, 3, 5) + bcb(123, 125, 145, 345) + bcbcb(12345)$$

$$C_i = 0 = c(2, 4, 6) + cbc(234, 236, 256, 456) + cbcbc(23456)$$

$$D_i = 1 + cb(23, 25, 45) + cbcb(2345)$$

The notation of Eq. (4-7) has been used in these equations.

Four sets of values which satisfy these relations are listed in the table of Fig. 4-21. The values of the elements of the ladder are given as a function of the parameters n and m, of a factor k which is used to adjust the impedance level, and of the factor A_i. The elements given in the last column are those used by $E.\,C.\,Ho$[37] in a method of synthsis.

4-5   TRANSFORMATION OF QUADRIPOLE MATRICES

The elements of any one of the six matrices of a quadripole can be expressed as functions of the elements of any other. It is only necessary to perform the inversion or transformation of a matrix of one type in order to obtain another. The relationships between the elements of the different matrices are given in the table of Fig. 4-22. These same relationships are easily obtained by transformations of the quadripole flow graphs. By transforming one type of matrix to

$$\begin{bmatrix} a_{11} \\ a_{12} \\ a_{21} \\ a_{22} \\ |a| \end{bmatrix} = \frac{1}{g_{21}}\begin{bmatrix} 1 \\ g_{22} \\ g_{11} \\ |g| \\ -g_{12} \end{bmatrix} = \frac{1}{y_{21}}\begin{bmatrix} -y_{22} \\ -1 \\ -|y| \\ -y_{11} \\ y_{12} \end{bmatrix} = \frac{1}{z_{21}}\begin{bmatrix} z_{11} \\ |z| \\ 1 \\ z_{22} \\ z_{12} \end{bmatrix} = \frac{1}{h_{21}}\begin{bmatrix} -|h| \\ -h_{11} \\ -h_{22} \\ -1 \\ -h_{12} \end{bmatrix} = \frac{1}{|b|}\begin{bmatrix} b_{22} \\ -b_{12} \\ -b_{21} \\ b_{11} \\ 1 \end{bmatrix}$$

$$\frac{1}{a_{11}}\begin{bmatrix} a_{21} \\ -|a| \\ 1 \\ a_{12} \\ a_{22} \end{bmatrix} = \begin{bmatrix} g_{11} \\ g_{12} \\ g_{21} \\ g_{22} \\ |g| \end{bmatrix} = \frac{1}{y_{22}}\begin{bmatrix} |y| \\ y_{12} \\ -y_{21} \\ 1 \\ y_{11} \end{bmatrix} = \frac{1}{z_{11}}\begin{bmatrix} 1 \\ -z_{12} \\ z_{21} \\ |z| \\ z_{22} \end{bmatrix} = \frac{1}{|h|}\begin{bmatrix} h_{22} \\ -h_{12} \\ -h_{21} \\ h_{11} \\ 1 \end{bmatrix} = \frac{1}{b_{22}}\begin{bmatrix} -b_{21} \\ -1 \\ |b| \\ -b_{12} \\ b_{11} \end{bmatrix}$$

$$\frac{1}{a_{12}}\begin{bmatrix} a_{22} \\ -|a| \\ -1 \\ a_{11} \\ a_{21} \end{bmatrix} = \frac{1}{g_{22}}\begin{bmatrix} |g| \\ g_{12} \\ -g_{21} \\ 1 \\ g_{11} \end{bmatrix} = \begin{bmatrix} y_{11} \\ y_{12} \\ y_{21} \\ y_{22} \\ |y| \end{bmatrix} = \frac{1}{|z|}\begin{bmatrix} z_{22} \\ -z_{12} \\ -z_{21} \\ z_{11} \\ 1 \end{bmatrix} = \frac{1}{h_{11}}\begin{bmatrix} 1 \\ -h_{12} \\ h_{21} \\ |h| \\ h_{22} \end{bmatrix} = \frac{1}{b_{12}}\begin{bmatrix} -b_{11} \\ 1 \\ |b| \\ -b_{22} \\ b_{21} \end{bmatrix}$$

$$\frac{1}{a_{21}}\begin{bmatrix} a_{11} \\ |a| \\ 1 \\ a_{22} \\ a_{12} \end{bmatrix} = \frac{1}{g_{11}}\begin{bmatrix} 1 \\ -g_{12} \\ g_{21} \\ |g| \\ g_{22} \end{bmatrix} = \frac{1}{|y|}\begin{bmatrix} y_{22} \\ -y_{12} \\ -y_{21} \\ y_{11} \\ 1 \end{bmatrix} = \begin{bmatrix} z_{11} \\ z_{12} \\ z_{21} \\ z_{22} \\ |z| \end{bmatrix} = \frac{1}{h_{22}}\begin{bmatrix} |h| \\ h_{12} \\ -h_{21} \\ 1 \\ h_{11} \end{bmatrix} = \frac{1}{b_{21}}\begin{bmatrix} -b_{22} \\ -1 \\ -|b| \\ -b_{11} \\ b_{12} \end{bmatrix}$$

$$\frac{1}{a_{22}}\begin{bmatrix} a_{12} \\ |a| \\ -1 \\ a_{21} \\ a_{11} \end{bmatrix} = \frac{1}{|g|}\begin{bmatrix} g_{22} \\ -g_{12} \\ -g_{21} \\ g_{11} \\ 1 \end{bmatrix} = \frac{1}{y_{11}}\begin{bmatrix} 1 \\ -y_{12} \\ y_{21} \\ |y| \\ y_{22} \end{bmatrix} = \frac{1}{z_{22}}\begin{bmatrix} |z| \\ z_{12} \\ -z_{21} \\ 1 \\ z_{11} \end{bmatrix} = \begin{bmatrix} h_{11} \\ h_{12} \\ h_{21} \\ h_{22} \\ |h| \end{bmatrix} = \frac{1}{b_{11}}\begin{bmatrix} -b_{12} \\ 1 \\ -|b| \\ -b_{21} \\ b_{22} \end{bmatrix}$$

$$\frac{1}{|a|}\begin{bmatrix} a_{22} \\ -a_{12} \\ -a_{21} \\ a_{11} \\ 1 \end{bmatrix} = \frac{1}{g_{12}}\begin{bmatrix} -|g| \\ g_{22} \\ g_{11} \\ -1 \\ -g_{21} \end{bmatrix} = \frac{1}{y_{12}}\begin{bmatrix} -y_{11} \\ 1 \\ |y| \\ -y_{22} \\ y_{21} \end{bmatrix} = \frac{1}{z_{12}}\begin{bmatrix} z_{22} \\ -|z| \\ -1 \\ z_{11} \\ z_{21} \end{bmatrix} = \frac{1}{h_{12}}\begin{bmatrix} 1 \\ -h_{11} \\ -h_{22} \\ |h| \\ -h_{21} \end{bmatrix} = \begin{bmatrix} b_{11} \\ b_{12} \\ b_{21} \\ b_{22} \\ |b| \end{bmatrix}$$

Fig. 4-22. Table of the matrices of a four-pole network

another, a new choice of independent and dependent variables must be made. Using the graphs, it suffices to effect one or two branch inversions in order to obtain new source nodes corresponding to the newly chosen independent variables.

In this manner, the a type matrix of Fig. 4-23a is transformed to a y type matrix by the inversion of branch a_{12}. This produces a new quadripole flow graph in which e_1 and e_2 become sources. This new graph is shown in Fig. 4-23b. It can subsequently be transformed to that of Fig. 4-23c in order to show the source and sink

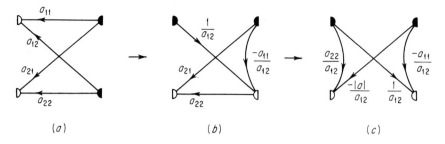

(a)   (b)   (c)

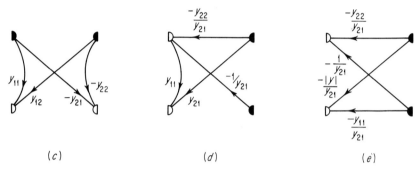

(c)   (d)   (e)

Fig. 4-23.   Transformation of a graph of type a into a graph of type y

$$y_{11} = \sum_{i=1}^{n} \frac{a_{22}^i}{a_{12}^i} \qquad\qquad -y_{12} = \sum_{i=1}^{n} \frac{|a^i|}{a_{12}^i}$$

$$-y_{21} = \sum_{i=1}^{n} \frac{1}{a_{12}^i} \qquad\qquad y_{22} = \sum_{i=1}^{n} \frac{a_{11}^i}{a_{12}^i}$$

$$|a| = a_{11}a_{22} - a_{12}a_{21} \qquad |y| = y_{11}y_{22} - y_{12}y_{21}$$

nodes more explicitly. The reverse transformation is given in Figs. 4-23c, d, and e.

The six different types of quadripole matrices have been introduced in order to simplify the interconnection of two or more quadripoles. If the proper matrix is chosen, the interconnection is a simple matrix operation. For example, the parallel connection of two quadripoles simply requires the addition of their y matrices. However, if these quadripoles are not already defined by their admittance matrices, then it is necessary to perform some matrix transformations before the required addition. Furthermore, if the final matrix is required to be of the same form as the original ones, the inverse transformation must be performed on the resultant matrix. Flow graphs will simplify this process without requiring that a complete graph of the network be drawn.

Consider the case of n quadripoles that are defined by their chain matrices but are connected in parallel. The chain matrix of the complete network is required. It is sufficient for this problem to consider the graphs of Fig. 4–23. There are n graphs like those of Fig. 4–23a in our problem; each must be transformed to the y form as in Fig. 4–23c. The y graphs are then connected to each other by superposition of corresponding source and sink nodes, and by addition of the transmittances of the parallel branches. The graph of Fig. 4–23d can thus be imagined as the residual graph of the complete network. From these graphs, the elements of the chain matrix of the complete network are obtained as functions of the elements of the chain matrix of each quadripole. For example, by inspection of Fig. 4–23e, the coefficient a_{11} is found to be:

$$a_{11} = -\frac{y_{22}}{y_{21}}$$

Each admittance of the Fig. d (the residual graph of the n graphs of Fig. c) is given by the equations of Fig. 4–23, so that the expression for the coefficient a_{11} of the complete network becomes:

$$-a_{11} = \frac{\displaystyle\sum_i \frac{a_{11}^i}{a_{12}^i}}{\displaystyle\sum_i \frac{1}{a_{12}^i}}$$

Any network consisting of n quadripoles all connected in the same way can be handled in this manner. If U^i indicates the matrix of an individual quadripole, and U is the matrix of the complete network, and if V is the most suitable matrix for this connection, the graph of U is drawn and is inverted to give the graph of V. The new graph (considered as the addition of the individual graphs) is then inverted, or else, it suffices to note, without drawing any graphs, upon what term U_{jk} of U the inversion is to be made, and then to apply the following rules:

1. Divide all the terms of the matrix U by U_{jk} which is then placed as a factor in the denominator of the matrix.

2. Replace the element that is diagonally opposite to the unit element in the matrix by its expression as a function of the determinant U.

3. Draw the summation sign $\sum$ before each factor of each expression.

If for example, the inversion is performed on U_{11} in the case of the connection of n quadripoles, the U matrix of the complete network becomes:

$$U = \frac{1}{\sum_i \frac{1}{U_{11}^i}} \left| \begin{array}{c|c} 1 & \sum_i \frac{U_{12}^i}{U_{11}^i} \\ \hline \sum_i \frac{U_{21}^i}{U_{11}^i} & \sum_i \frac{U_{12}^i}{U_{11}^i} \sum_i \frac{U_{21}^i}{U_{11}^i} + \sum_i \frac{1}{U_{11}^i} \sum_i \frac{|U^i|}{U_{11}^i} \end{array} \right| \tag{4-19}$$

If it is necessary to effect the graph inversion on two branches, the preceding rules are applied twice. As the U and V matrices are inverses of each other, the final result is:

$$U = \frac{\left| \begin{array}{cc} \sum \frac{U_{11}^i}{|U^i|} & \sum \frac{U_{12}^i}{|U^i|} \\ \sum \frac{U_{21}^i}{|U^i|} & \sum \frac{U_{22}^i}{|U^i|} \end{array} \right|}{\sum \frac{U_{11}^i}{|U^i|} \sum \frac{U_{22}^i}{|U^i|} - \sum \frac{U_{12}^i}{|U^i|} \sum \frac{U_{21}^i}{|U^i|}} \tag{4-20}$$

As an illustration of the method, the table of Fig. 4-24 gives the a matrices for n quadripoles connected in parallel-series (PS), parallel-parallel (PP), series-series (SS), and series-parallel (SP).

In the example of Fig. 4-25, the chain matrices of the subnetworks are written directly (by the method given in Sec. 4-4-1 for ladder networks) and the method described above is used to obtain directly the chain matrix of the complete network.

(a)

$$(a_{PS}) = \frac{1}{\sum_i \frac{1}{A_i}} \left[\begin{array}{c|c} 1 & \sum_i \frac{B_i}{A_i} \\ \hline \sum_i \frac{C_i}{A_i} & \sum_i \frac{B_i}{A_i} \sum_i \frac{C_i}{A_i} + \sum_i \frac{1}{A_i} \sum_i \frac{\Delta_i}{A_i} \end{array} \right]$$

(b)

$$(a_{PP}) = \frac{1}{\sum_i \frac{1}{B_i}} \left[\begin{array}{c|c} \sum_i \frac{A_i}{B_i} & 1 \\ \hline \sum_i \frac{A_i}{B_i} \sum_i \frac{D_i}{B_i} - \sum_i \frac{1}{B_i} \sum_i \frac{\Delta_i}{B_i} & \sum_i \frac{D_i}{B_i} \end{array} \right]$$

(c)

$$(a_{SS}) = \frac{1}{\sum_i \frac{1}{C_i}} \left[\begin{array}{c|c} \sum_i \frac{A_i}{C_i} & \sum_i \frac{A_i}{C_i} \sum_i \frac{D_i}{C_i} - \sum_i \frac{1}{C_i} \sum_i \frac{\Delta_i}{C_i} \\ \hline 1 & \sum_i \frac{D_i}{C_i} \end{array} \right]$$

(d)

$$(a_{SP}) = \frac{1}{\sum_i \frac{1}{D_i}} \left[\begin{array}{c|c} \sum_i \frac{B_i}{D_i} \sum_i \frac{C_i}{D_i} + \sum_i \frac{1}{D_i} \sum_i \frac{\Delta_i}{D_i} & \sum_i \frac{B_i}{D_i} \\ \hline \sum_i \frac{C_i}{D_i} & 1 \end{array} \right]$$

$$|a_{PS}| = \sum_i \frac{\Delta_i}{A_i} \Big/ \sum_i \frac{1}{A_i} \qquad |a_{SP}| = \sum_i \frac{\Delta_i}{C_i} \Big/ \sum_i \frac{1}{C_i} \qquad |a_{PP}| = \sum \frac{\Delta_i}{B_i} \Big/ \sum \frac{1}{B_i} \qquad |a_{SP}| = \sum_i \frac{\Delta_i}{D_i} \Big/ \sum_i \frac{1}{D_i}$$

Fig. 4-24. Chain matrix for n two-port networks connected in PS, PP, SS, and SP

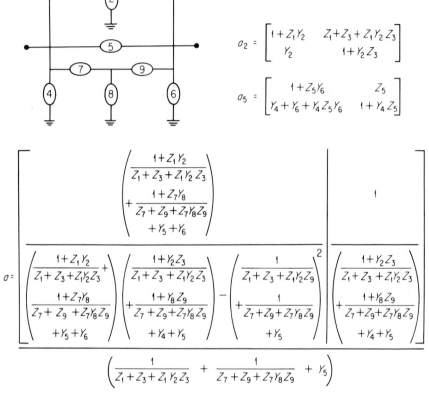

$$\sigma_2 = \begin{bmatrix} 1+Z_1Y_2 & Z_1+Z_3+Z_1Y_2Z_3 \\ Y_2 & 1+Y_2Z_3 \end{bmatrix}$$

$$\sigma_5 = \begin{bmatrix} 1+Z_5Y_6 & Z_5 \\ Y_4+Y_6+Y_4Z_5Y_6 & 1+Y_4Z_5 \end{bmatrix}$$

$$\sigma = \left[\begin{array}{c|c} \left(\dfrac{1+Z_1Y_2}{Z_1+Z_3+Z_1Y_2Z_3} + \dfrac{1+Z_7Y_8}{Z_7+Z_9+Z_7Y_8Z_9} + Y_5+Y_6\right) & 1 \\[4ex] \hline \left(\dfrac{\dfrac{1+Z_1Y_2}{Z_1+Z_3+Z_1Y_2Z_3}}{\dfrac{1+Z_7Y_8}{Z_7+Z_9+Z_7Y_8Z_9}} + Y_5+Y_6\right)\left(\dfrac{1+Y_2Z_3}{Z_1+Z_3+Z_1Y_2Z_3} + \dfrac{1+Y_8Z_9}{Z_7+Z_9+Z_7Y_8Z_9} + Y_4+Y_5\right) - \left(\dfrac{1}{Z_1+Z_3+Z_1Y_2Z_9} + \dfrac{1}{Z_7+Z_9+Z_7Y_8Z_9} + Y_5\right)^2 & \left(\dfrac{1+Y_2Z_3}{Z_1+Z_3+Z_1Y_2Z_3} + \dfrac{1+Y_8Z_9}{Z_7+Z_9+Z_7Y_8Z_9} + Y_4+Y_5\right) \end{array} \right]$$

$$\left(\dfrac{1}{Z_1+Z_3+Z_1Y_2Z_3} + \dfrac{1}{Z_7+Z_9+Z_7Y_8Z_9} + Y_5\right)$$

Fig. 4-25. Example of computation of the chain matrix

4-6 EXTENSION TO N-PORT NETWORKS

4-6-1. Generalization of quadripole flow graphs. The quadripole flow graphs can be generalized for n-port networks. It is necessary to draw one voltage node and one current node for each terminal-pair. The nodes of the graph are grouped in pairs to correspond to the pairs of variables at each port of the network. It is then possible to connect the graphs of the subnetworks in the same manner as these subnetworks are connected. If in an n-port network there are branches between each of the terminals, the graph will have a complex structure, corresponding to a matrix in which all the elements are nonzero. In most problems fortunately, not all these interconnecting branches exist. This does not reduce the degree of the

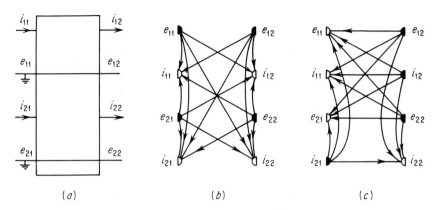

Fig. 4-26. Four-port network and two examples of graph for this network

matrix, but can considerably reduce the complexity of the graph by eliminating self-loops and reducing the index.

Two examples of multipole flow graphs are given in Figs. 4-26b and c, for a network of four terminal-pairs defined with respect to a reference terminal.

The independent and dependent variables are represented by half-nodes, as in the case of quadripole graphs. The rule for the interconnection of multipole flow graphs is the same as that for quadripole flow graphs. Only half-nodes of the same type can be superimposed, and only half-nodes of opposite types can be joined together to complete a node.

Once a multipole flow graph is obtained, all other multipole flow graphs corresponding to other choices of independent and dependent variables can be obtained from it. Such a transformation could be necessary when it is desired to connect two subnetworks, or in the case where an open path is required between two variables, in order to find a specified transfer function. Such a transformation could also be convenient in order to reduce the complexity of the graph by reducing its index. If the graph contains a large number of branches, it is not convenient to have to draw a new graph after each inversion. A method of inversion will now be described which allows the retention of the original graph by requiring only minor modifications.

In Fig. 4-27, a pair of nodes from Fig. 4-26b is drawn, and the path to be inverted is the open path from source to sink. In order to invert the branches of this path without disturbing the others, supplementary nodes and unit transmittances are introduced as shown

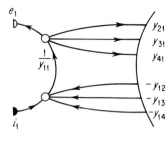

Fig. 4-27. Inversion at the input terminals of a multipole

in the figure. By applying the inversion rule of Chap. 1, the graph of Fig. 4-27b is obtained in which the directions of all the branches of the open path are reversed, and the other branches are not modified, except for the sign of the transmittances of the branches incident on the open path.

The same process applies to the inversion of an open path between any source and sink. The graph of Fig. 4-28a shows the cur-

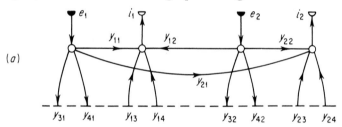

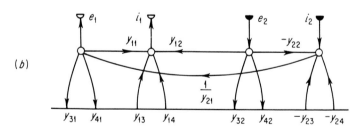

Fig. 4-28. Inversion of a path between the terminals of a multipole

rent and voltage nodes of two different ports of a network. Inversion of the open path e_1-i_2 gives the graph of Figure 4-28b. The arrows of the inverted path have been reversed, and the incident transmittances changed in sign.

For the inversion at a pair of terminals as in Fig. 4-27 one obtains from the inverted graph the expressions (with $m = 1$):

$$e_m = \frac{i_m}{y_{mm}} - \sum_k \frac{y_{mk}e_k}{y_{mm}}$$

$$i_j = \frac{y_{jm}i_m}{y_{mm}} + \sum_k \left(y_{jk} - \frac{y_{jm}y_{mk}}{y_{mm}}\right)e_k \qquad (k \neq m)$$

In the graph in which the dependent variables y_j and the independent variables y_k are related by:

$$y_j = \sum_k t_{jk}y_k; \quad k, j = 1, 2, 3, \ldots n$$

the inversion of a branch transmittance t_{ab} between source node x_b and sink y_a will give a new graph with y_a as a source and x_b as a sink. The part of the graph that is modified by the reversal corresponds to the equations:

$$x_b = \frac{1}{t_{ab}}y_a - \sum_k \frac{t_{ak}}{t_{ab}}x_k; \quad (k \neq b)$$

$$y_j = \frac{t_{jb}}{t_{ab}}y_a + \sum_k \left(t_{jk} - \frac{t_{ak}t_{jb}}{t_{ab}}\right)x_k$$

4-6-2. The generalized rotating machine. The generalized rotating machine studied by Kron[38] will be used as an application of multipole flow graphs. The graph is drawn from a diagram repre-

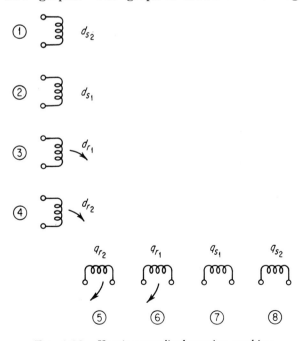

Fig. 4-29. Kron's generalized rotating machine

senting the windings of the machine, in order to associate directly the nodes of the graph to the variables at the terminals of the machine. Each connection in the machine will have its representation in the initial graph or in a modified one. Any required transfer function will be obtained directly by inspection of the graph. If a physical system has the same flow graph as the generalized rotating machine, it will be an analog of this machine. In particular, if this physical system is the setup diagram of an analog computer, it can be used to simulate the rotating machine. Thus, there exists a one-to-one correspondence between the elements of the machine (connections, terminal variables), and those of the graph and the analog model. This leads to a method of direct simulation, which will be discussed further in Chap. 5.

Fig. 4-29 presents a generalized rotating machine made up of two groups of coils at 90° to each other on two axes d and q. One group rotates with angular velocity $\dot{\theta}$ and the other group of coils is fixed. The subscript d refers to the direct axis and the subscript q to the quadrature axis.

Kron has shown that a rotating machine can be represented by a transient impedance tensor (tensor $\overline{Z}$ which will be found directly from the graph in Chap. 6). This tensor can be decomposed into a resistance tensor $\overline{R}$, an inductance $\overline{L} = \overline{L}_s + \overline{L}_r$ and a torque tensor $\overline{G} = \overline{G}_s + \overline{G}_r$:

$$\overline{R} = \begin{vmatrix} r_{ds2} & & & & & & & \\ & r_{ds1} & & & & & & \\ & & r_{r1} & & & & & \\ & & & r_{r2} & & & & \\ & & & & r_{r2} & & & \\ & & & & & r_{r1} & & \\ & & & & & & r_{qs1} & \\ & & & & & & & r_{qs2} \end{vmatrix}$$

$$\overline{L}_s = \begin{vmatrix} L_{ds2} & M_{ds} & M_{d12} & M_{d22} & & & & \\ M_{ds} & L_{ds1} & M_{d11} & M_{d21} & & & & \\ & & — & & & & & \\ & & — & & & & & \\ & & — & & & & & \\ & & — & & & & & \\ & & & & M_{q21} & M_{q11} & L_{qs1} & M_{qs} \\ & & & & M_{q22} & M_{q12} & M_{qs} & L_{qs2} \end{vmatrix}$$

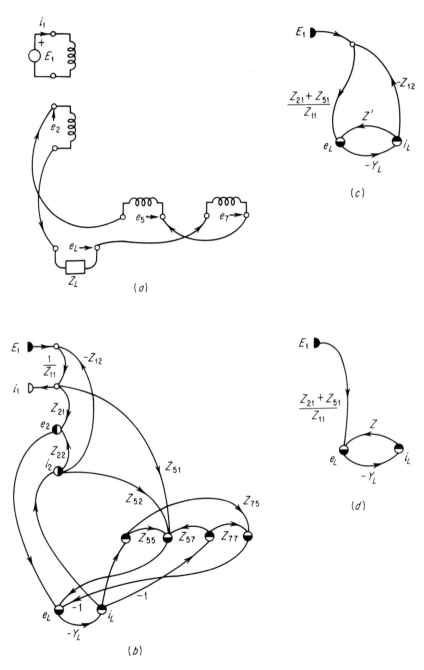

Fig. 4-30. Example of a compound generator

$$\bar{L}_r = \begin{vmatrix} \overline{} \\ \overline{} \\ M_{d12} & M_{d11} & L_{dr1} & M_{dr} \\ M_{d22} & M_{d21} & M_{dr} & L_{dr2} \\ & & & & L_{qr2} & M_{qr} & M_{q21} & M_{q22} \\ & & & & M_{qr} & L_{qr1} & M_{q11} & M_{q12} \\ & & & & & & \overline{} \\ & & & & & & \overline{} \end{vmatrix}$$

$$\bar{G} = \begin{vmatrix} \overline{} \\ \overline{} \\ & & & & \overline{} \\ & & & & M_{qr} & L_{qr1} & M_{q11} & M_{q12} \\ & & & & L_{qr2} & M_{qr} & M_{q21} & M_{q22} \\ -M_{d22} & -M_{d21} & -M_{dr} & -L_{dr2} \\ -M_{d12} & -M_{d11} & -L_{dr1} & -M_{dr} \\ \overline{} \\ \overline{} \end{vmatrix}$$

The transient impedance matrix is written as:

$$\bar{Z} = \bar{R} + \bar{L}p + \bar{G}p\theta$$

In order to simplify the notation, the elements of this matrix will be designated as Z_{ij} $(i, j = 1, 2, \ldots 8)$. A flow graph can be made to correspond to the matrix $\bar{Z}$. This graph is obtained from the diagram showing the actual connections of the machine.

Take, for example, the case of a compound generator (Fig. 4–30a) with coils 1, 2, 5 and 7. Then:

1. Connect coils 2, 5, and 7 in series with the load Z_L; suppose that coils 5 and 7 are in opposition.
2. Assume a voltage source E_1 in series with coil 1.
3. Consider the problem of finding the transfer function $\dfrac{i_L}{E_1}$, between E_1 and the load current.

Fig. 4–30b gives the graph corresponding to this problem. Note that the pair of nodes marked 1 has been transformed in order that the node E_1 becomes a source.

This graph gives the residual graph of Fig. 4–30c if the parallel branches from i_L to e_L are replaced by a single branch of transmittance Z':

$$Z' = Z_{22} + Z_{77} - Z_{75} + Z_{52} + Z_{55} - Z_{57}$$

By absorption of a node, the final graph of Fig. 4–30d is obtained and from this graph the desired result is:

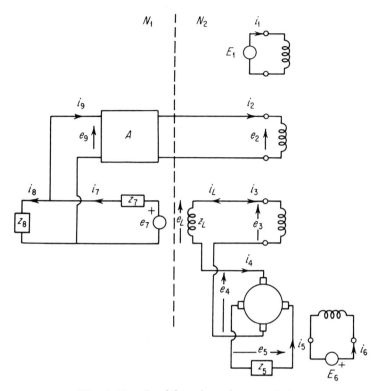

Fig. 4-31. Amplidyne for voltage regulation

$$\frac{i_L}{E_1} = \frac{Z_{21} + Z_{51}}{Z_{11}(Z_L + Z') - Z_{12}(Z_{21} + Z_{51})}$$

Consider now a slightly more complex example: an excitation system with amplidyne for automatic voltage regulation (Fig. 4-31). E_6 produces the primary field and E_1 is the reference voltage to which e_2 is compared. This last voltage is the d-c component of the voltage e_8 across the load which is to be maintained constant. A variation of Z_8 affects e_8 which produces a variation in e_2. If $E_1 + e_2$ is not zero, the resulting field produces a variation of i_5 which in turn causes a large variation of e_4 and thereby changes the excitation so as to bring e_8 back to its desired value. It is to be noted that the variables associated with N_1 (except the output of A) are alternating voltages and currents. The circuit N_1 is redrawn as indicated by Fig. 4-32. A flow graph of type h is chosen for network A (where A can be an active or passive network). Thus, this graph can be connected without modification to the terminals 2 of the graph of Fig. 4-33b. From Fig. 4-32c, one can write:

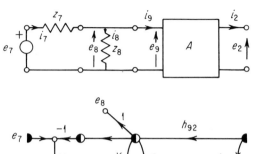

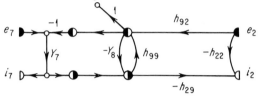

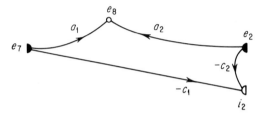

Fig. 4-32. Flow graph for the amplifier of Fig. 4-31

$$a_1 = y_7 h_{99} / D_1$$
$$a_2 = h_{92} / D_1$$
$$c_1 = y_7 h_{29} / D_1$$
$$c_2 = h_{22} - h_{92} h_{29}(y_7 + y_8) / D_1$$
$$D_1 = 1 + h_{99}(y_7 + y_8)$$

The network N_2 is represented in Fig. 4–33a by a multipole flow graph of type Z in which inversions have been made in the paths i_1-E_1 and i_6-E_6 in order to have E_1 and E_6 as sources. The load Z_5 is connected to port 5, and the ports 3 and 4 are connected in series. These connections are represented in the flow graph. The only variables of interest are E_1, E_6, e_2, i_2, and i_L, and so the flow graph will be reduced to retain only these nodes. The graph of Fig. 4–33b is obtained from Fig. 4–33a, by absorption of the nodes i_1 and i_6. It suffices for this to define the residual transmittances:

$$Z'_{jk} = Z_{jk} - \frac{Z_{j1}Z_{1k}}{Z_{11}} \qquad \begin{matrix} j = 2, 3, 4, 5 \\ k = 2, 3, 4 \end{matrix}$$

$$Z''_{j5} = Z_{j5} - \frac{Z_{j6}A_{65}}{Z_{66}} \qquad j = 4, 5$$

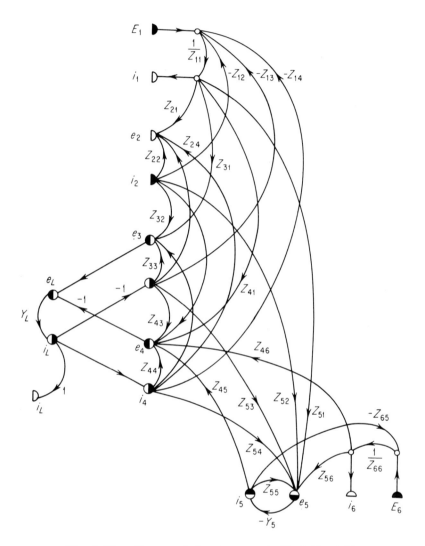

Fig. 4-33a. Flow graph for the network N_2 of Fig. 4-31

Further reductions lead to Fig. 4-34b. This last figure is the final graph for N_2, and the transmittances of this graph are defined by the following equations:

$$a_{21} = \frac{Z_{21}}{Z_{11}} + \frac{(Z'_{24} - Z'_{23})Y_L}{1 + Y_L Z}\left[\frac{Z_{31} - Z_{41}}{Z_{11}} + \frac{Z''_{45} Y_5 Z_{51}}{Z_{11}(1 + Y_5 Z''_{55})}\right]$$

$$a_{26} = \frac{(Z'_{24} - Z'_{23})Y_L}{1 + Y_L Z}\left[\frac{Z''_{45} Y_5 Z_{56}}{Z_{66}(1 + Y_5 Z''_{55})} - \frac{Z_{46}}{Z_{66}}\right]$$

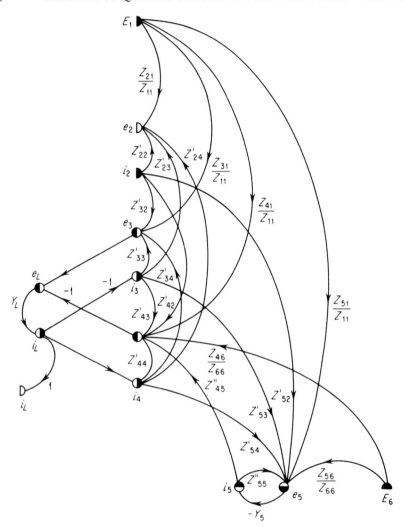

Fig. 4-33b. Reduction of the graph of Fig. 4-33a

$$Z_2 = Z'_{22} + \frac{(Z'_{24} - Z'_{23})\,Y_L\,(Z'_{32} - Z'_{42})}{1 + Y_L Z}$$

$$d_{L2} = Y_L \frac{(Z'_{32} - Z'_{42})}{1 + ZY_L}$$

$$Y_{L1} = \frac{Y_L}{1 + Y_L Z}\left[\frac{Z_{31} - Z_{41}}{Z_{11}} + \frac{Z''_{45}\,Y_5\,Z_{51}}{Z_{11}(1 + Y_5 Z''_{55})}\right]$$

$$Y_{L6} = \frac{Y_L}{1 + Y_L Z}\left[\frac{Z''_{45}\,Y_5\,Z_{56}}{Z_{66}(1 + Y_5 Z''_{55})} - \frac{Z_{46}}{Z_{66}}\right]$$

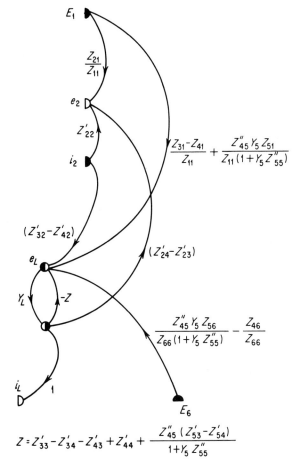

$$Z = Z'_{33} - Z'_{34} - Z'_{43} + Z'_{44} + \frac{Z''_{45}(Z'_{53} - Z'_{54})}{1 + Y_5 Z''_{55}}$$

Fig. 4-34a. Simplification of the graph of Fig. 4-33b

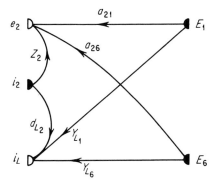

Fig. 4-34b. Final graph for the amplidyne

The residual graphs of N_1 and N_2 are connected together in Fig. 4-35 which represents in condensed form the equations of the amplidyne of Fig. 4-31. From Fig. 4-35, the voltage e_8 is directly obtained as a function of E_1 and E_6:

$$e_8 = \frac{A_1}{D}E_1 + \frac{A_6}{D}E_6$$

with:

$$A_1 = a_2[a_{21}(1 + c_1 d_{L2} Z_k) - (Z_2 c_1 Z_k Y_{L1})]$$
$$+ a_1 Z_k[Y_{L1}(1 + c_2 Z_2) - d_{L2} c_2 a_{21}]$$

$$A_6 = a_2[a_{26}(1 + c_1 d_{L2} Z_k) - (Z_2 c_1 Z_k Y_{L6})]$$
$$+ a_1 Z_k[Y_{L6}(1 + c_2 Z_2) - d_{L2} c_2 a_{26}]$$

$$D = 1 + c_2 Z_2 + c_1 Z_k d_{L2}$$

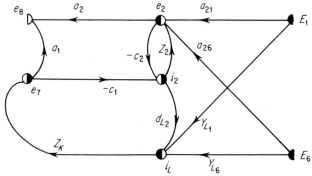

Fig. 4-35. Residual graph for the amplidyne voltage regulator

5

Direct Simulation on Analog Computers Through Signal Flow Graphs

5-1 INTRODUCTION

The simulation of physical systems with an analog computer generally requires first to write out the equations which describe the system, and then to establish an analog computer wiring diagram for the equations. For a complex system, this procedure can become painstaking and laborious.

For physical systems which can be considered to be made up of a number of simple interconnected elements, the method presented in this chapter makes it unnecessary to write the equations and permits the direct passage from the system under consideration to an analog computer setup diagram.

Each element of the system is represented by a computing unit in such a manner that all the terminal variables are indicated explicitly as they would be in the matrix or quadripole flow graph representation of that element. The operational units are then interconnected in the same manner as are the physical elements by making use of the rules for the interconnection of the flow graphs. Any or all of the variables can be retained, and each distinct parameter of the physical system has a corresponding element in the computer. If desired, the electrical analog network of the physical system can be obtained directly from the flow graph.

Although mechanical systems are used exclusively in the presentation of the method and in the examples, this method can be used for all lumped physical systems; for example, heat exchangers or acoustical systems composed of short tubes connected between cavities. The direct simulation method will be possible whenever an isomorphism can be established between the variables of a system and of an oriented topological graph. Trent[4] has shown that such a graph exists for all systems defined by two types of scalar variables such that: 1. these variables define the dynamical properties of each part of the system, when the value of the parameters is known; 2. the variables of the first type satisfy a "mesh law"; 3. the variables of the second type satisfy an "incidence law"; and 4. the dimensions of the product of the two types of variables are consistent.

It is not necessary, of course, that the system being studied be linear; the flow graphs in this chapter are used only as an analog model and are neither reduced nor transformed. These graphs may therefore contain branches having nonlinear or time-varying transmittances.

5-2 FLOW GRAPHS OF ELEMENTARY QUADRIPOLES

The quadripole flow graphs have been derived in Chap. 4 for the impedance, admittance, and mixed parameters. The same symbols and conventions will be used in the present chapter to represent the quadripoles which contain a single element. These quadripoles acquire a new interest now that the purpose is to replace each element of the physical system under consideration by an operational unit which corresponds to it. Since the equations of the mechanical ele-

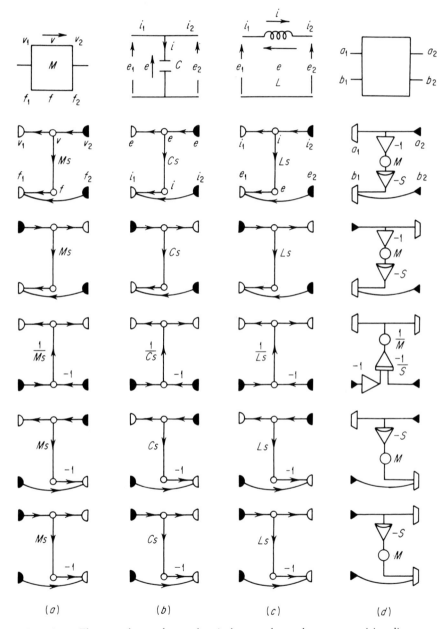

Fig. 5-1. Flow graphs, analogue electrical networks, and computer wiring diagram for a mass M

ments, mass, spring or dashpot, are analogous to the equations of the electrical elements, their flow graphs are similar and will be established together.

For the a type of flow graph which is presented in the first line of Fig. 5–1, and which corresponds to the cascade matrix, the equations can be written to show explicitly the variables associated with the element itself. For a mass M, a shunt condensor C, or a series inductance L, one can write:

$$f_1 = f + f_2 \quad f = Msv \quad v_1 = v = v_2 \tag{5-1}$$

$$i_1 = i + i_2 \quad i = Cse \quad e_1 = e = e_2 \tag{5-2}$$

$$e_1 = e + e_2 \quad e = Lsi \quad i_1 = i = i_2 \tag{5-3}$$

In these equations, the subscripts 1 and 2 refer to the corresponding terminals of the quadripole, and the quantities without subscripts refer to the variables associated with the particular element considered. It is assumed, of course, that for the mechanical elements the forces and velocities are taken along one reference axis. The quadripole representation of the elements defined by Eqs. (5–1, 2, 3) is given in the first row of Fig. 5–1. The flow graphs corresponding to these equations are of the same form for the three analogous elements and are drawn in the second row of the figure.

If the preceding equations are rewritten by using a different set of variables on the left-hand side, the other graphs of Fig. 5–1 can be derived from these equations. These graphs are graphs of type g, z, h, b, already introduced in Chap. 4. Fig. 5–1 contains all the possible types for the given elements. In any column, corresponding nodes represent the same variables. We can easily obtain all these graphs from any particular one by suitable inversions of open paths between a source and a sink node.

For a spring of value K, a reciprocal series inductance of value $\Gamma = 1/L$, or a shunt elastance of values $S = 1/C$, the following equations are obtained:

$$f_1 = f = f_2 \quad v = \frac{1}{K}sf \quad v_1 = v + v_2 \tag{5-4}$$

$$i_1 = i = i_2 \quad e = \frac{1}{\Gamma}si \quad e_1 = e + e_2 \tag{5-5}$$

$$e_1 = e = e_2 \quad i = \frac{1}{S}se \quad i_1 = i + i_2 \tag{5-6}$$

Fig. 5–2 shows these elements in quadripole form, the flow graphs corresponding to Eqs. (5–4, 5, 6) and the other forms obtained by inversion.

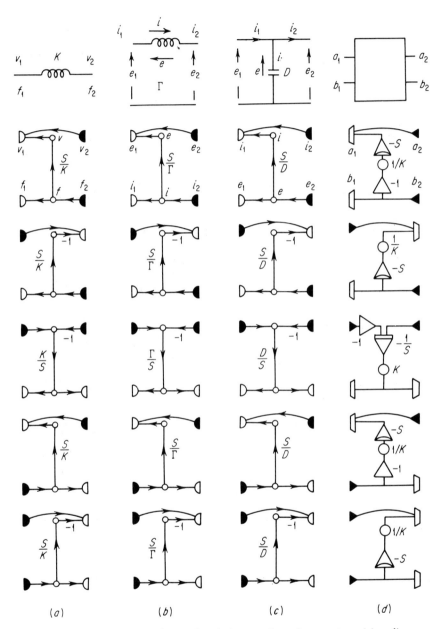

Fig. 5-2. Flow graphs, analogue electrical network, and computer wiring diagram for a spring K

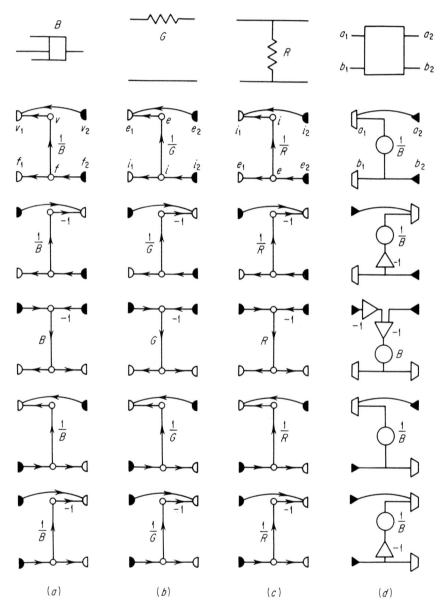

Fig. 5-3. Flow graphs, analogue electrical networks, and computer wiring diagram for a dashpot B

By proceeding in the same manner, the results indicated in Fig. 5-3 are obtained for the analogous elements: damping B, series conductance G, and shunt resistance R.

5-3 OPERATIONAL UNITS

5-3-1. Operational amplifier. The basic operational unit of an

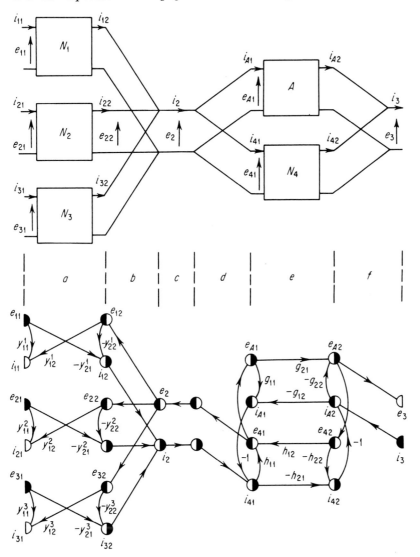

Fig. 5-4. Operational amplifier

analog computer consists in general of an amplifier A, a feedback network N_4, and one or more input networks N_1, N_2, N_3, connected as shown in the diagram of Fig. 5-4. To obtain the flow graph of this network, one can subdivide the network in Secs. a, b, c, ... f as shown in the figure and draw elementary graphs for each section as was shown in Chap. 4. It is convenient, as will be shown later, to take a flow graph of type g for the amplifier. As is usual, the voltages at the input of the networks will be chosen as source nodes and the output voltage will be taken as a sink node.

With this choice of terminal variables, and in order to maintain symmetry with respect to each input network, a y type of flow graph will be chosen for N_1, N_2, and N_3. The equations for Sec. a become then:

$$i_{k1} = y_{11}^k \underline{e_{k1}} + y_{12}^k \underline{e_{k2}}$$
$$- i_{k2} = y_{21}^k \underline{e_{k1}} + y_{22}^k \underline{e_{k2}} \qquad (k = 1, 2, 3) \qquad (5\text{-}7)$$

The flow graph for the interconnection of Sec. b is thus fixed according to the equations:

$$e_{12} = e_{22} = e_{32} = \underline{e_2}$$
$$\underline{i_2} = i_{12} + i_{22} + i_{32} \qquad (5\text{-}8)$$

With the g type of flow graph for the amplifier, along with the other choices, it is necessary to choose an h type of flow graph for the network N_4. The following equations are therefore obtained:

for Sec. d:

$$\underline{e_2} = e_{a1} = \underline{e_{41}}$$
$$i_{41} = \underline{i_2} - i_{a1} \qquad (5\text{-}9)$$

for amplifier A:

$$i_{a1} = g_{11}\underline{e_{a1}} - g_{12}\underline{i_{a2}}$$
$$e_{a2} = g_{21}\underline{e_{a1}} - g_{22}\underline{i_{a2}} \qquad (5\text{-}10)$$

for network N_4:

$$e_{41} = h_{11}\underline{i_{41}} + h_{12}\underline{e_{42}}$$
$$i_{41} = - h_{21}\underline{i_{41}} - h_{22}\underline{e_{42}} \qquad (5\text{-}11)$$

and for Sec. f:

$$e_{42} = \underline{e_3} = e_{a2}$$
$$i_{a2} = \underline{i_3} - i_{42} \qquad (5\text{-}12)$$

The underlined variables in these expressions designate sources (represented by black half-nodes) for each of the sections considered. It is unnecessary of course, to write out the equations since the graph of Fig. 5-4 contains the same information.

In general, operational amplifiers have a high gain and the para-

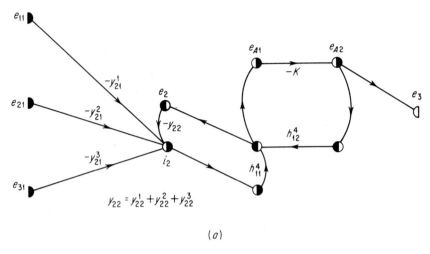

(a)

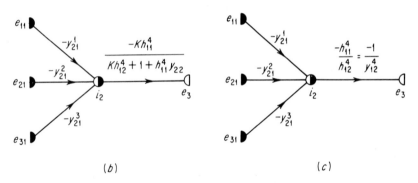

(b)   (c)

Fig. 5-5. Reduction of the graph of Fig. 5-4

meters g_{11}, g_{12}, and g_{22} are negligible. With the following notation:

$$g_{21} = -K$$
$$y_{22}^1 + y_{22}^2 + y_{22}^3 = y_{22} \tag{5-13}$$

the flow graph, after reduction to its index nodes, becomes that of Fig. 5-5a. Elimination of the loops gives the residual graph of Fig. 5-5b. A typical value for the gain K is of the order of 5×10^7; assuming K to be infinite, the transmittances indicated in Fig. 5-5c are obtained.

5-3-2. *Operational units.* To pass directly from a physical system to a corresponding analog computer model, the system will be considered to be composed of a number of elementary quadripole structures, each of which is represented by a corresponding operational unit. An operational unit consists of a number of operational elements connected in such a way as to simulate the quadripoles of the physical elements.

The operational elements, in general, consist of a high-gain amplifier and passive elements; that is, they are obtained from the network of Fig. 5-4 by choosing suitable passive networks. For example, from Fig. 5-5c the flow graphs for a summer and an integrator are obtained, as shown in Fig. 5-6a and b respectively. Also given in Fig. 5-6c is the graph corresponding to a potentiometer which is necessary to introduce scale factors. This figure also indicates the symbols which will be used to represent the elementary operators whose circuit diagrams are given in the first line. A differentiating element could also be derived in the same manner. However, this element is generally avoided because of the noise which it introduces in the computer.

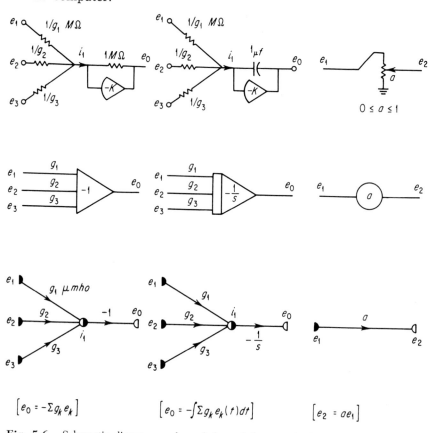

$$\left[e_0 = -\Sigma g_k e_k\right] \qquad \left[e_0 = -\int \Sigma g_k e_k(t)\,dt\right] \qquad \left[e_2 = a e_1\right]$$

Fig. 5-6. Schematic diagrams and symbols, and flow graphs for operational elements: adder, integrator, and scale factor

The operational units which are used in the direct simulation must contain the operational elements which simulate the transmittances of the flow graph of the physical system to be represented, and should be laid out in a quadripole form with a pair of variables at each terminal. Under these conditions, the graph of the operational unit is identical to the graph of the elementary quadripoles, since the former is derived from the latter. For a mass M, for example, the operational unit is given in the last column of Fig. 5-1. The variables a and b of this unit represent, with appropriate scaling, the velocities v and the forces f, respectively. The parameter M of the mass requires an elementary operator which is a potentiometer. The factor $1/s$ or s is represented by an integrator or a differentiator, respectively. The unit transmittances in the graph simply become connecting wires in the operational unit. The last column of Figs. 5-1, 2, 3, give the operational units which correspond to the elementary quadripole graphs which appear on the same row of the figure.

In order to simplify the interconnection of several operational units, and in order to maintain a correspondence between their terminal variables and those represented by the flow graph nodes, unit-gain amplifiers have been introduced.

These amplifiers are imagined to be separated into an input section and an output section, represented respectively by the base of the triangle and the black tip of Fig. 5-7. These two sections

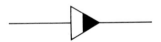

Fig. 5-7. Representation of the unit gain amplifier

correspond to the sink (white) and source (black) half-nodes of the quadripole flow graphs. When two operational units are connected together, the two parts of the unit-gain amplifiers are connected in the same manner as the corresponding half-nodes of the flow graph. In practice, when the amplifier is completed by the interconnection of its two parts, it can be eliminated if there is only one input. If there are several inputs, the amplifier can still be eliminated if there are a sufficient number of input terminals to the elements which follow this amplifier.

5-4   THE DIRECT SIMULATION PROCEDURE

The direct simulation of a physical system on an analog computer consists of:

1. the replacement of each element of the physical network by a corresponding operational unit.

2. the interconnection of these units in order to obtain the analog computer flow diagram.

Since the operational units previously described have a form identical to that of the quadripole flow graphs, these units can be connected and transformed in the same manner as the flow graphs. All the rules mentioned in the chapter on quadripoles remain valid for the interconnection of the operational units.

In practice, if one can perceive the physical system as consisting of the interconnection of simple elements, such as those described in Figs. 5-1, 2, 3, one can assemble the analog model directly without drawing the flow graph, by imagining the graphs of the operational elements, and by replacing each element of the physical system by its corresponding operational unit. In other cases, it will be neces-

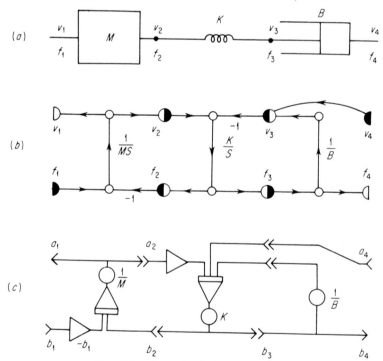

Fig. 5-8.   Example of direct simulation

sary first to draw the graph formed by the interconnection of subgraphs in the same way as the quadripoles are interconnected. From
these graphs, the analog model is then obtained directly since the
operational units possess an identical form of graph. The complete
graph becomes, in fact, the desired analog model.

Fig. 5-8 illustrates a simple example consisting of a mass M, a
spring K, and a dashpot B. For illustration, the force f_1 and the
velocity v_4 are chosen as the independent variables or as the sources
of the flow graph. Several graphs can be drawn for the same physical system; however, if it is desired to avoid differentiators it will
be necessary to choose a convenient type of graph for the mass and
spring elements. Such a graph is shown in Fig. 5-8b, along with
the analog model (Fig. 5-8c) which is obtained directly from it. In
this last figure, the unit-gain amplifiers have been removed since it
has been supposed, as is usual, that the integrators have several input
terminals. In order to indicate the terminals of the operational units,
these units have been joined through connectors. The electrical analog networks of the physical system can be deduced directly from
the flow graph of Fig. 5-8b. In the first network of Fig. 5-9, the
voltages and currents are the quantities analogous to the velocities
and the forces, whereas the inverse situation applies to the second
network. The electrical analog of Fig. 5-9a is more convenient to
use in complex problems since it can be obtained by the direct substitution of the electrical elements C, Γ and G, for the mechanical
elements M, K, and B, respectively. This comes from the fact that
the equations for the forces and velocities at the junctions of this

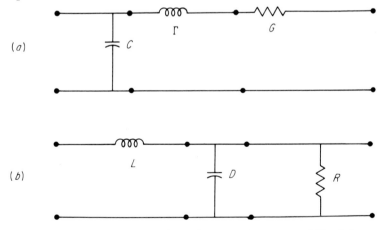

Fig. 5-9. Electrical networks analogous to the system of Fig. 5-8

physical system have the same form as the nodal equations for the currents and voltages of the electrical network. For this reason, the structure of the electrical network is the same as that of the physical system.

An example has been given in Fig. 5-10 in which the physical elements are connected in cascade and in parallel. The flow graph

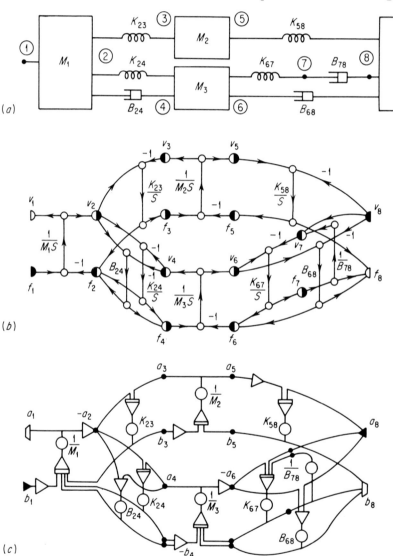

Fig. 5-10. A mechanical system, its flow graph and the corresponding computer setup diagram

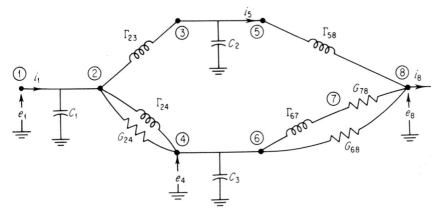

Fig. 5-11. Analogous network for the system of Fig. 5-10

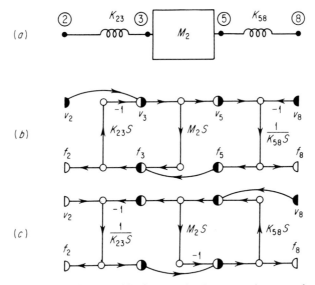

Fig. 5-12. Other possible flow graphs for some elements of the system of Fig. 5-10

of Fig. 5-10b is formed, in a direct manner, by the interconnection of the elementary quadripoles which correspond to the individual physical elements. In the same manner, the analog model of Fig. 5-10c is formed by the interconnection of corresponding analog computer units. The same, of course, applies to the electrical analog of Fig. 5-11. At those junctions at which only two elements are connected, such as junctions 3, 5, 7 of Fig. 5-10a, different types of quadripole flow graphs can be used. For example, for the elements K_{23}, M_2, and K_{58} connected to junctions 2, 3, 5, 8, either the flow graph of Fig. 5–12 or the one actually indicated in Fig. 5–10b can be used. The only rule of interconnection is, in effect, that the junctions being connected must have the same velocity and that the sum of the forces must be zero. In an analogus manner, in the electrical network of Fig. 5–11, the terminals connected together must have the same voltages and the sum of the currents at a node must be zero. From the point of view of the flow graphs, this signifies that a node which represents a velocity or voltage variable must have only one incoming branch, and that a node which represents a force or current variable must have only one outgoing branch. These nodes have already been defined as distributive and contributive, respectively. For example, junction 2 of the graph of Fig. 5–10b depicts a contributive node whose equation is:

$$- f_{M_1} = f_{K_{23}} + f_{K_{24}} + f_{B_{24}} \tag{5-14}$$

and a distributive node whose equation is:

$$v_{M_1} = v_{K_{23}} = v_{K_{24}} = v_{B_{24}} \tag{5-15}$$

Instead of using f_{M_1} as a sink and v_{M_1} as a source, the following combinations could have been used: $(f_{K_{23}}, v_{K_{23}})$; $(f_{K_{24}}, v_{K_{24}})$; or $(f_{B_{24}}, v_{B_{24}})$, always with the restriction that a "force or current" node must be contributive and that a "velocity or voltage" node must be distributive. The other possible graphs for a given system can be obtained from any particular one by suitable inversions of open and closed paths. In this way, at least seventy-six different flow graphs could be obtained for the system given in Fig. 5–10, by applying all possible inversions on the graph of Fig. 5–10b. If it is desired to avoid the differentiator as an elementary operational element, it is necessary to reject the graphs which contain transmittances of value s.

5-5 PRACTICAL CONSIDERATIONS

The scale factors for the variables and for time can be introduced in the operational units themselves. Thus, for the velocity and force variables one writes:

$$a = k_1 v \tag{5-16}$$

$$b = k_2 f \tag{5-17}$$

where a and b are the voltages which are analogous to the variables v and f. The scale factors k_1 and k_2 have the dimensions of volts per unit of velocity and of volts per unit of force, respectively. The scale factors are chosen so that the amplifiers operate within their linear range, usually between $- 100$ and $+ 100$ volts. A change of scale can also be applied to a particular amplifier by multiplying all its inputs by a scale factor k_3, and by dividing all its outputs by the same factor. The output variable would now have a scaling k_3 times the previous one, the rest of the analog model being unaffected. Time scaling can be done by replacing s by Ts or by dividing all inputs to a differentiator by T and by multiplying all inputs to an integrator by T. If T is greater than unity, the solution time is slowed down by a factor T.

If it is desired to retain all the force and velocity variables in the analog model, no reduction in the number of amplifiers is possible except, perhaps, for some amplifiers if the sign of their variables is of no particular interest (see for example Fig. 5-10c). After listing the variables that it is explicitly desired to retain, for recording purposes for example, it is sometimes possible to reduce the number of amplifiers. This reduction depends on the system under consideration, on the types of graph used, and on the experience of the programmer. The number of amplifiers can also be reduced by using additional units built up according to the model of Fig. 5-4, with more complex passive circuits in order to obtain more complex transfer functions. It is not possible to reduce the number of potentiometers, however, if it is required to vary individually each parameter of the system.

In many cases, there are two possible types of electrical analogs for a given physical system. This comes from the fact that there may exist two dual electrical networks having the same form of equations. In the analog computer model, there is only one type of variable and so there can be only one type of computer representation for each element of the physical system. If, at the same time, it is desired to avoid differentiators in the analog setup, then there is only one form of computer unit which can be used for each mass and spring. This can be seen in Figs. 5-1 and 5-2, in which there exists only one computing unit that contains an integrator. These integrators can of course have applied to them initial conditions which correspond to the initial conditions that exist in the physical system.

Direct simulation, with the help of flow graphs, permits the direct passage from a physical system to a flow graph or to an analog computer model which simulates the physical system. This is done by interconnecting elementary computing units in the same way as elementary quadripoles are interconnected in the study of complex electrical networks. However, the restrictions which apply to the interconnections of the electrical networks[32] do not appear in the direct simulation procedure. Effectively, it suffices to ensure that the nodes which represent the force variables are contributive nodes and that those which represent velocity variables are distributive nodes, so that the force-velocity relations are automatically satisfied at each junction in the interconnection of the subgraphs.

Although in this presentation of the direct simulation procedure, the discussion has been restricted to mechanical systems which are reducible to the interconnection of quadripoles, the same methods can be applied to more general cases. Instead of considering a flow graph in the form of a quadripole, the elementary graphs, corresponding to those of Figs. 5-1 and 5-2, would become graphs with as many pairs of nodes as there are different variables. For example, three nodes would be used for each force and velocity in an elementary graph which represents a mechanical element which can move in three-dimensional space. Within this graph, we would find a transmittance Ms for a mass or for a spring, as well as nonlinear transmittances to represent the resolution of the forces, velocities, and displacements between the reference axis and the axis of each particular element. To these more complex elementary graphs, there would correspond operational units made up of amplifiers, integrators, and resolvers as well as the other operational elements already described. The interconnection of such elementary structures, however, would also be as simple as the interconnection of the quadripole flow graphs, as was shown in the generalization to n-port networks in Chap. 4. If it is not desired to retain all the variables, these graphs can be reduced according to the reduction methods described previously. This reduction should, however, retain the nodes which are attached to branches whose transmittances are not linear.

6

Applications of
Flow Graphs to
Electrical Machine Theory

6-1 INTRODUCTION

Flow graphs, whose usefulness is easily seen when applied to electrical networks, also prove to be a useful tool for the study of electrical machines and transformers. In this chapter, several examples are presented which will show the advantages of this method.

In the first part of this chapter, the real transformer will be analyzed. This study will show how flow graphs simplify the derivation of known results and lead directly to the establishment of setup diagrams for analog computers.

The second part is dedicated to the study of rotating machines. During the last twenty-five years, this branch of electrical engineering has reached a high degree of unity, due in a large measure, to Gabriel Kron. He, in fact, introduced the idea of a "generalized electrical machine," which is at the same time the simplest and the most general machine possible. Physical considerations allow the study of any other electrical machine using the "generalized" one as a basis.

To this end, Kron used tensor calculus and established a means of representing machines by "transient impedance matrices," which were defined from the primitive machine by using "connection matrices"[38].

It seemed interesting to the authors to illustrate Kron's theory, by means of signal flow graphs. This technique does not pretend to bring about new results, but it has the advantage over tensor calculus in that it renders tangible—and in a way, visible—the relationships between the different parts of the machines. Moreover, the graphs that are obtained are in fact equivalent to the setup diagrams used in analog computers and lead easily to the direct simulation of rotating machines.

6-2 REAL TRANSFORMERS

6-2-1 Definitions. Consider a two-winding transformer, with a finite magnetizing inductance. It is assumed that its behavior is linear, but this restriction will be removed later by showing how it is possible to account for saturation in a detailed study with an analog computer.

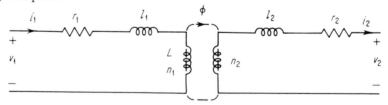

Fig. 6-1. Real transformer

The first step is to establish the flow graph of a transformer whose equivalent circuit is given in Fig. 6-1; in which the following symbols appear:

   v_1 and v_2: the values of the instantaneous voltages across the primary and secondary,

   i_1 and i_2: the instantaneous currents in the primary and secondary,

   r_1 and r_2: the resistances of these windings,

   l_1 and l_2: the leakage inductances of these windings,

n_1 and n_2: the number of turns of the primary and secondary,

Lp: the magnetizing inductance seen from the primary circuit, and

φ: the instantaneous flux which is common to the two windings.

If one introduces an ideal transformer, with a turns ratio of $m = \dfrac{n_2}{n_1}$, the diagram of the real transformer becomes that of Fig.

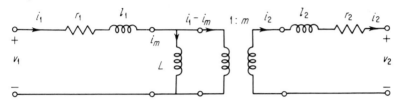

Fig. 6-2. Equivalent network of the real transformer

6-2. This transformer can thus be considered as a cascade connection of the following quadripoles: a series impedance $r_1 + l_1p$, a shunt impedance Lp, an ideal transformer, and a series impedance $r_2 + l_2p$. Consider the transformer energized by a constant voltage v_1 and a variable load current i_2; v_1 and i_2 will be taken as independent variables. Under these conditions, it is then possible to combine the graphs of the elementary quadripoles, using the methods and nota-

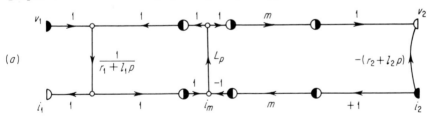

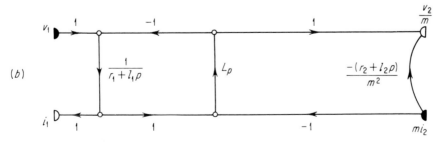

Fig. 6-3. Flow graphs for the transformer under no-load conditions

tions presented in Chap. 4. One possible representation is given in Fig. 6-3a. After evident simplifications, the graph of Fig. 6-3b is obtained.

6-2-2. *Study of a transformer under no-load conditions.* By putting $i_2 = 0$ in the graph of Fig. 6-3b, the representation of a real transformer under no-load is obtained. The no-load voltage ratio and the total primary impedance can be derived immediately, by applying Mason's rule. In fact, there is only one loop of transmittance $\dfrac{-Lp}{r_1 + l_1p}$ and so the following results are easily written:

1. No-load voltage ratio:

$$\frac{v_2}{mv_1} = \frac{Lp/(r_1 + l_1p)}{1 + Lp/(r_1 + l_1p)} \qquad (6\text{-}1)$$

from which one gets:

$$\frac{v_2}{v_1} = \frac{mLp}{r_1 + (L + l_1)p} \qquad (6\text{-}2)$$

In the permanent sinusoidal state, the no-load voltage ratio is:

$$\frac{V_2}{V_1} = \frac{mjL\omega}{r_1 + j(L + l_1)\omega} \qquad (6\text{-}3)$$

Evidently, this ratio is independent of the leakage in the secondary. If it is assumed, as is usually the case, that the absolute value of the denominator is close to $(L + l_1)\omega$, the expression for the voltage ratio reduces to:

$$\frac{V_2}{V_1} = m \frac{L}{L + l_1} = \frac{m}{\nu_1} \qquad (6\text{-}4)$$

where:

$$\nu_1 = \frac{L + l_1}{L} \qquad (6\text{-}5)$$

ν_1: being the Hopkinson coefficient of the primary.

2. No-load impedance:

From the graph of Fig. 6-3, one can write:

$$\frac{1}{z_0} = \frac{i_1}{v_1} = \frac{1/(r_1 + l_1p)}{1 + Lp/(r_1 + l_1p)} = \frac{1}{r_1 + (L + l_1)p}$$

$$z_0 = r_1 + (L + l_1)p \qquad (6\text{-}6)$$

In the permanent sinusoidal state, this expression becomes:

$$Z_0 = r_1 + j\omega(L + l_1) \qquad (6\text{-}7)$$

6-2-3. *Study of a transformer under short-circuit conditions.* One has now to set the secondary voltage v_2 to zero. It is therefore necessary to consider v_2 as an independent variable. However, it is also convenient to take i_1 as an independent variable, since during a short-circuit test, this current is adjusted to its nominal value, and v_1 is measured. This last quantity will then appear as a sink in the flow graph.

One of the possible representations using the quadripole flow graphs and satisfying these conditions is given in Fig. 6-4a.

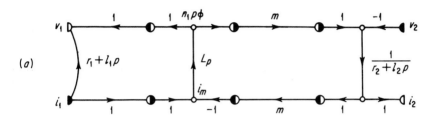

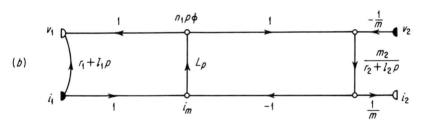

Fig. 6-4. Graphs for the transformer under short-circuit conditions

By setting the voltage v_2 equal to zero, and after obvious simplifications the flow graph of Fig. 6-4b results.

By proceeding in a manner similar to that of Sec. 6-2-2, the current ratio under short-circuit condition and the short-circuit impedance are computed.

The loop of the graph has a transmittance $\left(\dfrac{-m^2 Lp}{r_2 + l_2 p}\right)$

1. Short-circuit current ratio: Applying Mason's rule, one finds:

$$\frac{m i_2}{i_1} = \frac{m^2 Lp / (r_2 + l_2 p)}{1 + m^2 Lp / (r_2 + l_2 p)} \tag{6-8}$$

$$\frac{i_2}{i_1} = \frac{mLp}{r_2 + (l_2 + m^2 L)p} \tag{6-9}$$

The current ratio under short-circuit condition is independent of the leakage inductance of the primary. In the sinusoidal steady-state, this ratio becomes:

$$\frac{I_2}{I_1} = \frac{mjL\omega}{r_2 + j(l_2 + m^2L)\omega} \tag{6-10}$$

If it is assumed, as is generally the case, that the absolute value of the denominator is close to $\omega(l_2 + m^2L)$, the current ratio can be written:

$$\frac{I_2}{I_1} = \frac{1}{m}\left(\frac{L}{L + l_2/m^2}\right) = \frac{1}{mv_2} \tag{6-11}$$

with:

$$v_2 = \frac{L + l_2/m^2}{L} \tag{6-12}$$

v_2 is the Hopkinson coefficient for the secondary.

2. Short-circuit impedance: Mason's rule leads to the following equations:

$$\frac{v_1}{i_1} = (r_1 + l_1 p) + \frac{Lp}{1 + m^2 Lp/(r_2 + l_2 p)} \tag{6-13}$$

$$\frac{v_1}{i_1} = \frac{p^2[l_1(l_2 + m^2L) + l_2L] + p[r_1(l_2 + m^2L) + r_2(L + l_1)] + r_1 r_2}{p(l_2 + m^2L) + r_2} \tag{6-14}$$

or in the sinusoidal steady-state:

$$\frac{V_1}{I_1} = \frac{r_1 r_2 - \omega^2[l_1(l_2 + m^2L) + l_2L] + j\omega[r_1(l_2 + m^2L) + r_2(L + l_1)]}{r_2 + j\omega(l_2 + m^2L)} \tag{6-15}$$

If the magnetizing inductance is much greater than the leakage inductances referred to the primary, the preceding expression reduces to:

$$\frac{V_1}{I_1} = r_1 + \frac{r_2}{m^2} + j\omega\left(l_1 + \frac{l_2}{m^2}\right) \tag{6-16}$$

6-2-4. *Direct simulation of a real transformer.* Two examples of setup diagrams permitting the study of a real transformer on an analog computer will now be given:

1. Example 1: Study of the transient behaviour of a transformer whose secondary is connected to a resistive load R_e.

The following assumptions are made: a. the primary voltage is an independent variable; b. the diagram must permit the study of the apparatus when the magnetizing inductance L approaches zero. This condition prohibits the use of the quadripole flow graphs which contain a transmittance $1/L$.

The graph of Fig. 6–5a is one possible representation of the problem under study.

First, all the values are referred to the primary. Then all trans-

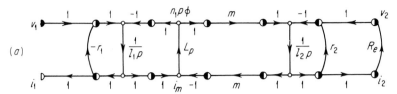

Fig. 6-5a. Interconnection of quadripole flow graphs for the transformer (first example)

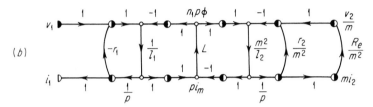

Fig. 6-5b. Modified graph to obtain a computer wiring diagram

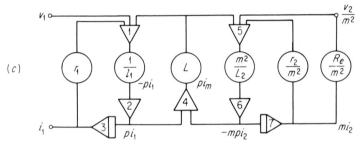

Fig. 6-5c. Computer wiring diagram for the transformer

mittances containing p in the numerator are eliminated in order to avoid the use of differentiators which are generally shunned in analog computation. This operation leads to the replacement of the magnetizing current i_m by its time derivative. It is thus necessary to show explicitly the time derivatives of i_1 and mi_2; this is done by a displacement of the factor $1/p$, as shown in Fig. 6-5b.

Fig. 6-5c is the computer setup obtained from the preceding graph, after having taken into account the sign reversals introduced by the operational amplifiers.

2. Analog study of a transformer taking into account the effect of saturation.

The preceding study does not allow one to consider the effect of saturation. A representation of this effect requires that the flux linkage $n_1\varphi$ and the magnetizing current i_m be shown explicitly, because there exists a nonlinear relation between these two quantities.

Consider a transformer loaded by a capacitance C and assume

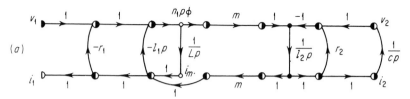

Fig. 6-6a. Interconnection of quadripole flow graphs for the transformer (second example)

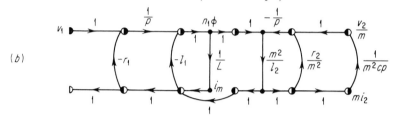

Fig. 6-6b. Modifications of the flow graphs to obtain a computer wiring diagram

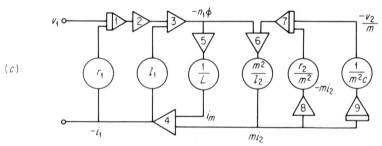

Fig. 6-6c. A second computer wiring diagram for the real transformer

that the analog computer contains a function generator allowing the calculation of i_m when the value of $n_1\varphi$ is known.

A suitable initial graph is that of Fig. 6-6a (because of the orientation of the branch of transmittance $1/Lp$). One can then refer all the values to the primary circuit and rearrange the factors p in the transmittances to obtain the graph of Fig. 6-6b.

The computer setup of Fig. 6-6c follows immediately. It is possible to replace amplifier 5 and potentiometer $1/L$ by the function generator, in order to represent the effect of saturation.

6-3 STUDY OF ROTATING MACHINES

6-3-1. Basic theory. The study of rotating machines, as envisaged by Kron, will be reviewed now by means of flow graphs.

It will be necessary, in the first place, to establish the graph representing a simple coil moving in a magnetic field.

After a brief review of properties of the generalized machine, a flow graph is established which contains as transmittances the elements of the transient impedance matrix. From this graph is derived a flow graph representing the torque equations. These graphs will be called respectively "transient impedance flow graph" and "torque flow graph."

The graphs representing the connections required to relate the generalized machine to real ones will then be studied. A few examples, results, and computer setups for several machines will also be given.

6-3-2. Representation of a moving coil in a magnetic field. Consider a moving coil of resistance R, traversed by a current i resulting from a voltage e across its terminals. Suppose further that this coil rotates in a magnetic field with angular velocity $\dot{\theta}$.

The voltage applied to the coil must equal the sum of the three voltages:

1. the voltage drop Ri in the coil.
2. the counterelectromotive force $p\varphi$ induced by the variation of the magnetic flux linked by the coil.
3. the counterelectromotive force $\dot{\theta}\psi$ caused by the rotation of the coil at velocity $\dot{\theta}$ in a flux ψ.

The equation defining the behavior of the moving coil is thus:

$$e = Ri + p\varphi + \dot{\theta}\psi \qquad (6-17)$$

The graph of Fig. 6-7a represents Eq. (6-17). If the magnetic field ψ is not varying with time, the variable flux φ linked by the coil is thus $\varphi = Li$, as depicted by the graph of Fig. 6-7b.

The energy-balance equation is obtained by multiplying both sides of Eq. (6-17) by the current i:

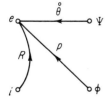

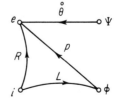

Fig. 6-7a. Flow graph to represent the electrical conditions of a moving coil in a magnetic field

Fig. 6-7b. Introduction of the self-inductance of the coil

$$ei = Ri^2 + ip\varphi + i\dot{\theta}\psi \qquad (6\text{-}18)$$

The product ei is the electric power supplied to the coil. The term Ri^2 represents the losses in the conductors. The variation of magnetic energy stored in the coil is $ip\varphi$ and the term $i\dot{\theta}\psi$ represents the available mechanical energy. If the instantaneous electromagnetic torque is designated by f, the mechanical power can also be written as $f\dot{\theta}$, and thus leads to the expression for the torque:

$$f = i\psi \qquad (6\text{-}19)$$

The complete graph is given in Fig. 6-8.

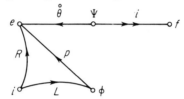

Fig. 6-8. Flow graph showing the electrical conditions and the electromagnetic torque on a coil in a magnetic field

These results can now be generalized by defining the "generalized electric machine."

6-3-3. The generalized electric machine. Consider a two-pole electric machine, whose stator is made up of windings placed along two orthogonal fixed axes Od and Oq. These axes are called the "direct axis" and the "quadrature axis" (or "transverse axis"). Fig. 6-9a is a schematic diagram of this machine.

The windings are designated by three indices. The first index is d for the windings along the direct axis, and q for the windings along the quadrature axis. The second index s identifies a stator or rotor winding. The windings are numbered in order along each axis, starting with the one closest to the air gap. The third index refers to the position of a particular winding.

The rotor is a smooth rotor consisting of a lap winding with two parallel paths and a commutator. Two diametrically opposite brushes on each axis define two equivalent rotor coils $dr1$ and $qr1$ whose axes coincide with Od and Oq. These definitions could be generalized by considering a rotor with several concentric windings and several commutators. These windings would then be defined as $dr2, dr3, \ldots$ and $qr2, qr3, \ldots$

The discussion will be limited to the case of a single rotor winding. Furthermore, it is convenient to adopt the following conventions:

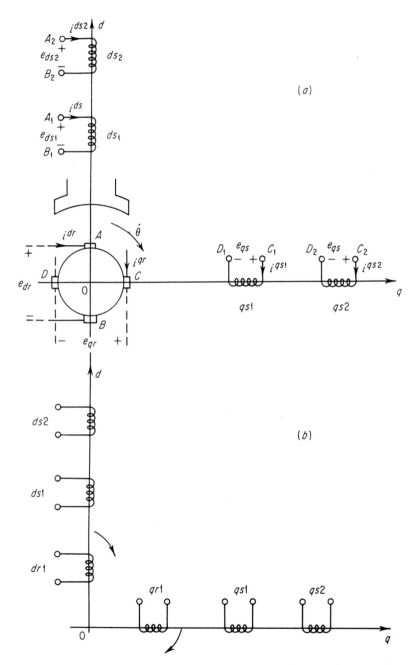

Fig. 6-9. Generalized rotating machine: (a) schematic diagram (b) network representation

1. According to Kron's assumptions, the machine rotates in a clockwise direction.
2. The reference marks for the voltages are given in Fig. 6-9a.
3. The reference direction for the currents will be into the terminal marked +. The rotor currents will thus be positive only when the machine operates as a motor.
4. The flux distribution is considered to be sinusoidal along the air gap.
5. The windings of the rotor are in such a direction that a current entering brush A will create a magnetic field that is in the same direction as one which would be created by a current entering the A_1 and A_2 terminals of the stator windings. In other words, the rotor coil is wound in such a way that brush A is homologous with terminals A_1 and A_2 of the stator. The same convention is valid for the quadrature axis, for which the homologous terminals are C, C_1, C_2.

In Fig. 6-9b, the machine is drawn in a more schematic manner by replacing the rotor windings by their equivalent coils. The arrows beside the equivalent coils indicate that these are windings in which electromotive forces can be set up by the motion of the conductors in the direct or quadrature fields.

Each of the coils constituting the generalized rotating machine can be represented by a flow graph similar to that of Fig. 6-8, provided the following considerations are taken into account:

1. The flux φ_α related to a given winding α, is created by the fields of the currents of all the windings on the same axis. The contribution to this flux from the winding α itself is given by $L_\alpha i^\alpha$, where L_α is the self-inductance of the winding. The contributions

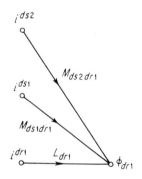

Fig. 6-10. Example of a flow graph for the evaluation of the flux linkage of a coil

of the other windings will be given by terms of the form $M_{\alpha\beta}i^\beta$ where $M_{\alpha\beta}$ is the mutual inductance between winding α and any other winding β on the same axis.

Fig. 6-10 shows, for example, how to represent the flux φ_{dr1} corresponding to the rotor winding on the direct axis.

2. Only the graphs corresponding to the rotor windings will have branches of transmittance $\dot{\theta}$. This is obvious, since only the rotor windings will be sources of generated electromotive forces.

3. There is a relationship between the fluxes φ and ψ for the rotor windings, which will be established presently.

Refer to Fig. 6-11a, where it is supposed that only the windings of the direct axis are excited, creating a flux φ_d. With the sign conventions given above, the electromotive force e_1 appearing between

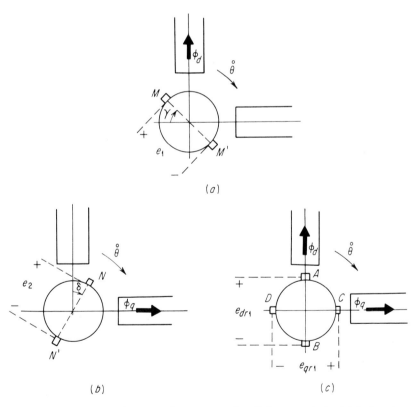

Fig. 6-11. Relations between the armature flux linkages and the total flux in the generalized machines in the following cases: (a) excitation of the coil of the direct axis; (b) excitation of the coil of the transverse axis; (c) normal operation of the generalized machine

two diametrically opposite brushes $M'M$, at an angle γ to the neutral axis, is expressed by the following equation:

$$e_1 = \frac{N}{2\pi}\dot{\theta}\varphi_d \cos\gamma + \frac{N}{2\pi}p\varphi_d \sin\gamma \qquad (6\text{-}20a)$$

where N is the total number of armature conductors, these being assumed uniformly 'distributed.

In the same way, one finds for the case of Fig. 6-11b:

$$e_2 = \frac{N}{2\pi}\dot{\theta}\varphi_q \cos\delta + \frac{N}{2\pi}p\varphi_q \sin\delta \qquad (6\text{-}20b)$$

When a flux exists along both axis, that is, when the windings of both axes are excited, the electromotive forces e_{dr1} between brushes B and A and e_{qr1} between brushes D and C are:

$$e_{dr1} = e_1\left(\gamma = \frac{\pi}{2}\right) + e_2 \qquad (\delta = 0)$$

$$e_{qr1} = e_1\,(\gamma = \pi) + e_2 \qquad \left(\delta = \frac{\pi}{2}\right) \qquad (6\text{-}21)$$

or:

$$e_{dr1} = \frac{N}{2\pi}p\varphi_d + \frac{N}{2\pi}\dot{\theta}\varphi_q$$

$$e_{qr1} = -\frac{N}{2\pi}\dot{\theta}\varphi_d + \frac{N}{2\pi}p\varphi_q \qquad (6\text{-}22)$$

In order to establish the flow graphs for the rotor windings in a manner similar to that which has been used for a single coil, the sum of the counterelectromotive forces created between the brushes must be written:

$$e_{dr1} = p\varphi_{dr1} + \dot{\theta}\psi_{dr1}$$

$$e_{pr1} = p\varphi_{qr1} + \dot{\theta}\psi_{qr1} \qquad (6\text{-}23)$$

In these expressions, φ_{dr1} is the flux linked by the winding $dr1$. The time-variation of this flux gives rise to the so-called "induced electromotive force." The flux ψ_{dr1} cut by the winding $dr1$, produces a so-called "generated electromotive force." The quantities φ_{qr1} and ψ_{qr1} are defined in a similar manner for the winding $qr1$.

Comparing Eqs. (6-22) and (6-23), one finds that:

$$\varphi_{dr1} = -\psi_{qr1} = \frac{N}{2\pi}\varphi_d$$

$$\varphi_{qr1} = \psi_{dr1} = \frac{N}{2\pi}\varphi_q \qquad (6\text{-}24)$$

Fig. 6-12 represents a flow graph containing all the relationships

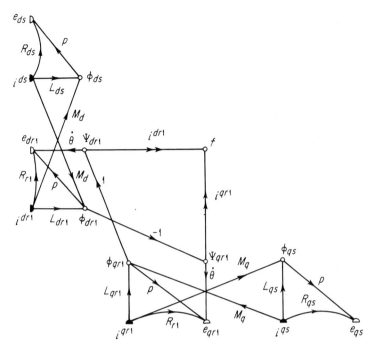

Fig. 6-12. Flow graph of a generalized rotating machine

established up to now. In order to simplify the figure, it has been
assumed that the machine has only one stator winding on each axis.
It is to be noted that the resistance between brushes placed diametrically opposite on a uniform rotor is independent of the position
of these brushes. This resistance is R_{r1}. The mutual inductance between the windings of the direct axis is M_d, and that between the
windings of the quadrature axis is M_q. The other resistances and
inductances are designated by their corresponding winding indices.

For convenience, the voltage and current nodes of the flow graph
have been drawn in relative positions suggestive of the disposition
of the windings in the schematic diagram (Fig. 6-9).

If the various fluxes, φ and ψ are not of particular interest, the
absorption of the nodes representing these fluxes will give the flow
graph of Fig. 6-13a, which is called the "transient impedance flow
graph." This graph may be obtained directly in the following manner:

1. The voltage and current nodes of the various windings are
distributed along two perpendicular axes according to the physical
position of these windings.

2. For each winding, the node i is connected to the node e by

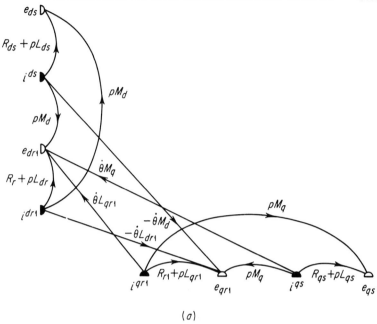

Fig. 6-13a. Flow graph for the transient impedances of
the generalized machine

a branch of transmittance $R + Lp$, R and L being the resistance and
inductance of the given winding.

3.   The node i of each winding is connected to the voltage nodes
of all the other windings on the same axis, by branches of transmittance pM, where M is the mutual inductance between the windings whose nodes i and e are connected.

4.   From all the i nodes on the direct axis, branches are drawn
to the rotor voltage nodes on the quadrature axis.   The transmittance of any of these branches is found in the following manner:

Find the transmittance of the branch leaving some i node and
ending at the direct axis e node which has the same index as the
quadrature axis e node under consideration.   This transmittance contains a term in p.   The required transmittance will be the product
of $-\dot{\theta}$ by the coefficient of the term in p found above.

Although the present discussion is limited to a machine containing only one rotor winding on each axis, this method is valid for
any number of rotor windings.

5.   The operation described above is performed for the current
nodes on the quadrature axis, this time multiplying the transmittances
by $+\dot{\theta}$ instead of $-\dot{\theta}$.

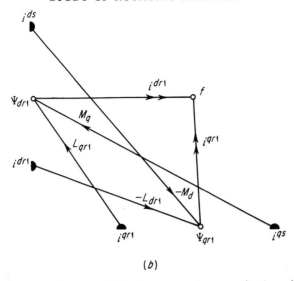

Fig. 6-13b. Flow graph for the torque of a generalized machine

The relationships allowing the calculation of torque can be presented apart from the others, as in Fig. 6–13b.

Torque is deduced from the transient impedance flow graph by keeping only the terms containing the velocity $\dot{\theta}$, and by dividing the branch transmittances by $\dot{\theta}$. Further, on this graph the rotor voltages are replaced by the corresponding fluxes ψ. The torque is thus the sum of the ψi's corresponding to the rotor. This graph will be called "torque flow graph."

6-3-4. Representation of connections and changes of reference axes. The generalized machine has been defined by a transient impedance flow graph and a torque flow graph which show explicitly the electromagnetic properties of the machine. It is now necessary to show how one can apply these graphs to the study of real machines. Kron has used a "connection matrix" to express the following conditions:

1. Certain windings of the generalized machine can be connected together electrically to make up a real machine (shunt or series motor for example). As for passive circuits, one can define the connection matrix C by expressing the currents of the generalized machine (represented by a vector i) as functions of the currents in the real machine (represented by a vector i') by means of Kirchhoff's equations. These relationships, in matrix form, are written as:

$$i = C \cdot i' \qquad (6\text{–}25)$$

The conservation of energy requires the following equation for the voltages:

$$e' = C_T e \qquad (6\text{-}26)$$

where C_T is the transposed matrix of C

    e is the column vector representing the voltages of the generalized machine

    e' is the column vector representing the voltages of the real machine.

If Z and Z' are the transient impedance matrices of the generalized and real machines respectively, Z' can be related to Z by:

$$Z' = C_T Z C \qquad (6\text{-}27a)$$

The same relationship applies to the torque matrices G and G'.

$$G' = C_T G C \qquad (6\text{-}27b)$$

2. In certain cases, the currents of the generalized machine are considered as the components along two axes of the currents of the real machine. This is the case, for example, for a d-c generator with brushes shifted from the neutral position; the rotor current can be decomposed into direct current and quadrature current. Here again, it is possible to define a connection matrix by expressing the linear relationships between the real machine currents and those of the generalized machine.

Flow graphs will be used to represent the linear relationships defined in Eqs. (6-25) and (6-26). These "connection flow graphs" will play the same role as Kron's connection matrices, and will allow the derivation of impedance and torque flow graphs of real machines. This technique will now be illustrated in several examples.

6-3-5. Series machines. The schematic diagram of a series machine is shown in Fig. 6-14a. To study this machine, consider a generalized machine having one stator winding ds and one rotor winding qr. With the indicated connections, the equations relating the generalized machine to the real one are:

$$i^{ds} = i^{qr} = i$$
$$e = e_{ds} + e_{qr} \qquad (6\text{-}28)$$

The transient impedance flow graph of this machine is shown in Fig. 6-14b. This graph is obtained from that of the generalized machine by considering only the windings ds and qr, and by expressing the relationships in Eq. (6-28) in flow graph form. This process is similar to that used by Kron in establishing a Z matrix (Eq. 6-27a).

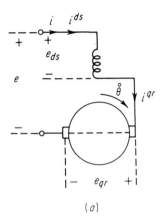

(a)

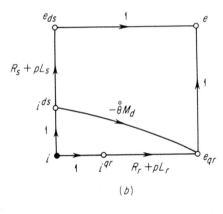

(b)

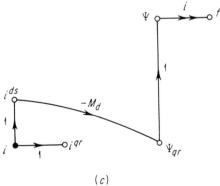

(c)

Fig. 6-14. (a) Series generator; (b) graph showing the transient impedances;
(c) graph for the torque

From Fig. 6-14b, the transient impedance can be written by inspection:

$$\frac{e}{i} = (R_s + R_r - \dot{\theta}M_d) + p(L_r + L_s) \tag{6-29}$$

The term $-\dot{\theta}M_d$ in Eq. 6-29 shows that if the speed $\dot{\theta}$ is high enough, the machine can be considered as presenting a negative resistance. If the condition $R_s + R_r - \dot{\theta}M_d \leqq 0$ is realized, the voltage build-up is obtained when the machine is short-circuited.

The torque flow graph of Fig. 6-14c is obtained from that of Fig. 6-14b by the process described in Sec. 6-3-3. One can thus write the torque equation directly:

$$f = -M_d i^2 \tag{6-30}$$

The minus sign means that it is a resistive torque, which is evident since the connections have been chosen such that the machine could act as a generator.

As an example, the reader can in a similar fashion establish the corresponding graphs for a motor, using: $i^{ds} = -i^{qr} = i$ and $e = e_{ds} - e^{qr}$. It can thus be verified that if the velocity is positive the build-up of voltage is impossible.

In order to complete this example, the analog circuit for the series machine will now be given.

By separating the machine parameters, the graph of Fig. 6-14b becomes that of Fig. 6-15a. One obtains the graph of Fig. 6-15b by reversing the path e-e_{ds}-pi^{ds}-i, and by taking into account the relation $pi^{ds} = pi^{qr}$.

The analog computer setup in Fig. 6-15c is deduced from the graph of Fig. 6-15b by changing the signs of certain transmittances to account for the sign reversal introduced by the amplifiers. Note that the loop through amplifier 5 has an even number of amplifiers. This fact corresponds to an exponential increase of current if $\dot{\theta}M_d$ has a high enough value. This is thus the analog equivalent of the build-up of voltage of a series generator.

Although it is possible to simplify this setup, it is preferable to present it in this more detailed form, since all quantities are placed directly in evidence.

6-3-6. Direct current machine with brushes shifted from the neutral. Fig. 6-16a shows a direct current machine whose brush axis makes an angle α with the neutral axis. The rotor field, which is directed along the brush axis, can be decomposed along the direct axis and the quadrature axis. A decomposition of the rotor field

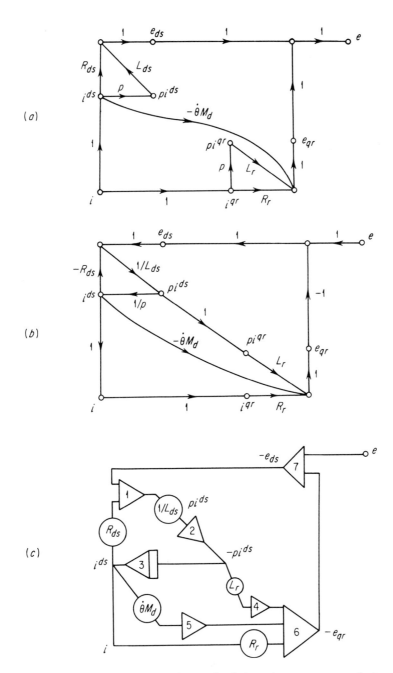

Fig. 6-15. Transformations of the graph of the series generator to obtain a computer wiring diagram

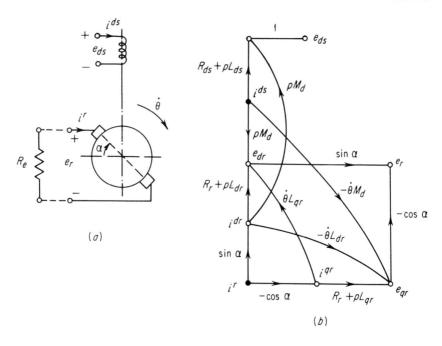

(a)

(b)

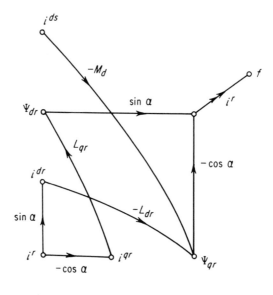

(c)

Fig. 6-16. (a) generator with brushes shifted from the neutral point;
(b) flow graph for the transient impedances;
(c) flow graph for the torque

along these axes is in effect a decomposition of the current. This condition is expressed by the equations:

$$i^{dr} = i^r \sin \alpha$$
$$- i^{qr} = i^r \cos \alpha$$

(6-31)

The energy balance equation gives:

$$e_{dr} i^{dr} + e_{qr} i^{qr} = e_r i^r$$
$$e_{dr} i^r \sin \alpha - e_{qr} i^r \cos \alpha = e_r i^r$$

(6-32)

$$e_r = e_{dr} \sin \alpha - e_{qr} \cos \alpha$$

(6-33)

These equations lead to the transient impedance flow graph in Fig. 6-16b, and the torque flow graph of Fig. 6-16c. This torque flow graph allows a direct calculation of the electromagnetic torque for a direct current machine with brushes shifted from the neutral:

$$f = (L_{dr} - L_{qr})(i^r)^2 \sin \alpha \cos \alpha + M_d i^{ds} i^r \cos \alpha$$

(6-34)

If the rotor is excited by a voltage e_r, and if the stator is not connected, there exists a torque:

$$f = \frac{L_{dr} - L_{qr}}{2} (i^r)^2 \sin 2\alpha$$

(6-35)

This torque is zero in the case of a machine without salient poles, for which $L_{dr} = L_{qr}$.

Conversely, in the case of salient poles, rotation of the machine is possible without excitation. The torque is zero for shifts of $k\pi / 2$, and is maximum for shifts of $\pi / 4 + k\pi / 2$. As the salient poles

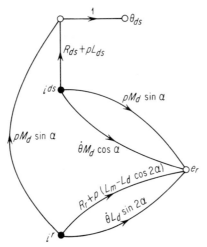

Fig. 6-17. Reduction of the graph for the transient impedances fo Fig. 6–16b

are on the direct axis, L_{dr} is always greater than L_{qr}, and the direction of the torque is that of the shift of the brushes from the neutral axis.

Consider now that the machine acts as a generator, feeding a resistance R_e. From the graph of Fig. 6-16b, the Fig. 6-17 is obtained by putting:

$$L_m = \frac{L_{dr} + L_{qr}}{2}$$

$$L_d = \frac{L_{dr} - L_{qr}}{2}$$

$$(6\text{-}36)$$

In order to express all the parameters, the graph of Fig. 6-18a contains the time derivatives of the currents in that part of the graph representing the machine. It also uses Ohm's law to represent the external circuit with the conventions shown in Fig. 6-9, given by:

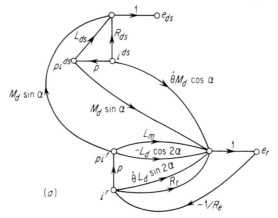

Fig. 6-18. (a) Transformation of the transient impedance graph of the generator with the brushes shifted from the neutral point

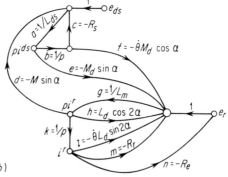

(b) Final graph for the generator with the brushes shifted

$$e_r = - R_e i^r \qquad (6\text{-}37)$$

The inversion of the paths $e_{ds}, p i^{ds}, i^{ds}$ and $e_r, p i^r, i^r$ leads to the graph of Fig. 6-18b.

The response of the generator to an applied voltage e_{ds} on the stator is given by applying Mason's rule to the last graph:

$$\frac{i^r}{e_{ds}} = \frac{N}{D} \qquad (6\text{-}38)$$

with:

$$N = abfgk + aegk \qquad (6\text{-}39)$$

$$\begin{aligned} D = 1 - \ & (abc + abfgd + aegd + gh + gkl + gkm + gkn) \\ & + (abcgh + abcgkl + abcgkm + abcgkn) \end{aligned} \qquad (6\text{-}40)$$

By replacing the transmittances by their values, one gets:

$$\frac{i^r}{e_{ds}} = - M_d \left(\frac{\dot{\theta} \cos \alpha + p \sin \alpha}{A_1 p^2 + B_1 p + C_1} \right) \qquad (6\text{-}41)$$

with:

$$A_1 = L_{ds}(L_m - L_d \cos 2\alpha) - M_d^2 \sin 2\alpha$$

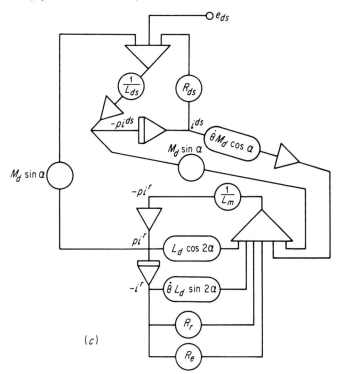

(c) Computer wiring diagram

$$B_1 = R_{ds}(L_m - L_d \cos 2\alpha) + L_{ds}(R_r + R_e + \dot{\theta} L_d \sin 2\alpha)$$
$$- \dot{\theta} M_d^2 \sin \alpha \cos \alpha \qquad (6\text{-}42)$$
$$C_1 = R_{ds}(R_r + R_e + \dot{\theta} L_d \sin 2\alpha)$$

In the steady-state, the rotor current is:

$$i^r = \frac{- M_d \dot{\theta} \cos \alpha e_{ds}}{C_1} = \frac{- \dot{\theta} M_d \cos \alpha e_{ds}}{R_{ds}(R_r + R_e \dot{\theta} L_d \sin 2\alpha)} \qquad (6\text{-}43)$$

The setup diagram deduced from Fig. 6-18b is presented in Fig.
6-18c. It is to be noted that this diagram is valid only if the quantities $\sin \alpha$, $\cos \alpha$, $\sin 2\alpha$ and $\cos 2\alpha$ are positive, that is, for values
of α between 0 and $\pi/4$. For other values of brush shift, one must
introduce appropriate sign changers in the circuits containing the
trigonometric terms.

6-3-7. *Uncompensated Metadyne.* Fig. 6-19a represents a metadyne with one stator winding. The quadrature axis brushes are
short-circuited, and the load R_e is connected between the brushes of
the direct axis. The flow graph of this machine is identical to that
for a generalized machine with three windings: *ds, dr* and *qr* (Fig.
6-19b). However, the condition that $e_{qr} = 0$ necessitates that e_{qr} be
chosen as the independent variable. On the "transient admittance
flow graph" of Fig. 6-20a, the paths e_{ds}, pi^{ds}, e_{dr}, pi^{dr} and e_{qr}, pi^{qr} are
inversions of corresponding paths in the graph of Fig. 6-19b. In

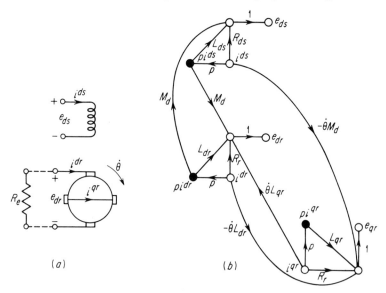

Fig. 6-19. (a) Uncompensated metadyne; (b) its graph for the transient
impedances

addition, the connection to the external circuit is represented by the branch transmittance $-R_e$, directed from i^{dr} to e_{dr}.

A practical problem that is often encountered is to determine the response of the generator to a variation of excitation voltage. Mason's rule gives:

$$\frac{i^{dr}}{e_{ds}} = \frac{N}{D} \tag{6-44}$$

with:

$$N = begl\,(1 - nqu) + bcdunmgl \tag{6-45}$$

$$\begin{aligned}
D = 1 &- (abc + glh + glk + bcdunmgf + begf + mglrun + nqu) \\
&+ (abcglh + abcglk + abcmglrun + abcnqu + glhnqu \\
&+ glknqu + begfnqu) - (abcglhnqu + abcglknqu) \tag{6-46}
\end{aligned}$$

Replacing the transmittances by their values in Eqs. (6-44) to (6-46) gives:

$$\frac{i^r}{e_{ds}} = -M_d \frac{p^2 L_{qr} + pR_r + \dot{\theta}^2 L_{qr}}{A_1 p^3 + B_1 p^2 + C_1 p + D_1} \tag{6-47}$$

with:

$$\begin{aligned}
A_1 &= L_{qr}(L_{ds}L_{dr} - M_d^2) \\
B_1 &= (R_r + R_e)L_{ds}L_{qr} + L_{dr}(R_{ds}L_{qr} + R_r L_{ds}) - R_r M_d^2 \\
C_1 &= \dot{\theta}^2 L_{qr}(L_{ds}L_{dr} - M_d^2) \\
&\quad + (R_r + R_e)(R_{ds}L_{qr} + R_r L_{ds}) + R_{ds}R_r L_{dr} \tag{6-48} \\
D_1 &= R_{ds}R_r(R_r + R_e) + \dot{\theta}^2 R_{ds}L_{dr}L_{qr}
\end{aligned}$$

In the steady-state, the current fed by the machine into the load resistance is:

$$i^r = \frac{-M_d \dot{\theta}^2 L_{qr} e_{ds}}{D_1} = \frac{-\dot{\theta}^2 M_d L_{qr} e_{ds}}{R_{ds}R_r(R_r + R_e) + \dot{\theta}^2 L_{dr}L_{qr}R_{ds}} \tag{6-49}$$

The terms in $\dot{\theta}^2$ show that, for a fixed voltage e_{ds}, the current is independent of the direction of rotation.

The complete analog diagram for an uncompensated metadyne (Fig. 6-20b) is directly deduced from Fig. 6-20a.

6-3-8. "Cross" transformer Metadyne. Fig. 6-21 represents a "cross" transformer metadyne. This machine consists of a d-c rotor connected to two mutually perpendicular sets of brushes, with no stator windings. It is assumed that the rotor inductance L is independent of the brush position (isotropic metadyne).

The transient impedance flow graph for that machine is the graph of the generalized machine reduced to two rotor windings (Fig. 6-21b).

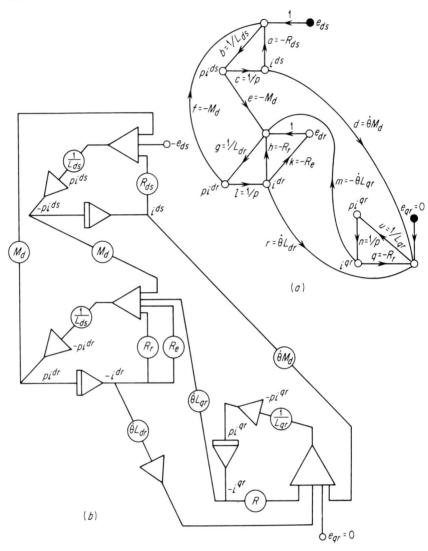

Fig. 6-20. (a) Transformation of the graph of the metadyne to obtain a computer wiring diagram; (b) Computer wiring diagram for the uncompensated metadyne

The torque flow graph of Fig. 6-21c follows immediately and shows that the electromagnetic torque is zero.

$$f = i^{qr} L i^{dr} - i^{dr} L i^{qr} = 0 \qquad (6\text{-}50)$$

According to the usual notation, let:

$$e_1 = e_{qr}$$

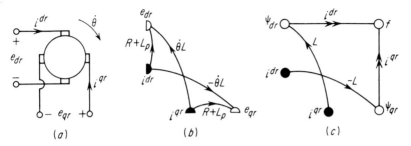

Fig. 6-21. (a) Cross transformer-metadyne; (b) its graph for the transient impedances; (c) its graph for the torque

$$e_2 = e_{dr}$$
$$i_1 = i^{qr} \tag{6-51}$$
$$i_2 = -i^{dr}$$

Fig. 6-22 becomes the new transient impedance flow graph.

If this machine is considered as a quadripole, the graph of Fig. 6-22 shows that it can be regarded as a series connection of two

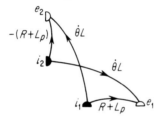

Fig. 6-22. A new graph for the transient impedances of the cross transformer metadyne

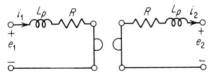

Fig. 6-23. Equivalent representation of the cross transformer-metadyne

impedances $R + Lp$, with a gyrator between them (Fig. 6-23).

In order to establish the equivalent diagram of this metadyne, the secondary circuit must be transformed by duality. With this transformation, the principal use of this machine becomes obvious; that is, it allows a constant current source to be obtained from a constant voltage source.

Note that, in addition, if the secondary terminals are short-circuited the response to a variation of input voltage e_1 could be in the form

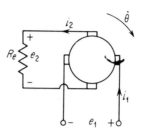

Fig. 6-24. Cross transformer-metadyne connected to an external load

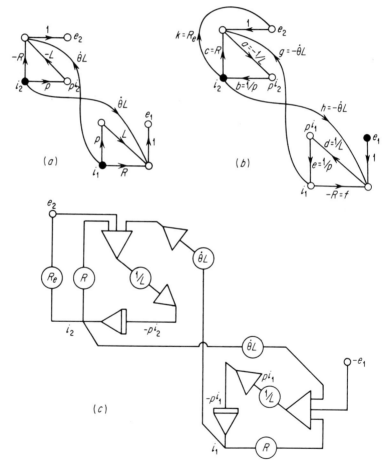

Fig. 6-25. (a) Transformation of the graph of the metadyne; (b) Final graph for the transformer-metadyne; (c) Computer wiring diagram for the transformer-metadyne

of damped oscillations. This is apparent from the equivalent diagram of the machine, remembering that the secondary inductance is transformed into a capacitance in the primary.

The working of the "cross"; metadyne transformer can be studied in more detail, when it is connected to a load R_e (Fig. 6-24).

The graph of Fig. 6-25a represents the unconnected machine. In Fig. 6-25b the paths e_2, pi_2, i_2 and e_1, pi_1, i_1 have been inverted. The external load is represented by a branch of transmittance R_e.

The current in the secondary can be calculated from the primary voltage:

$$\frac{i_2}{e_1} = \frac{N}{D} \qquad (6\text{-}53)$$

with:

$$N = degab$$

$$D = 1 - (abc + abk + def + abhdeg) + (abcdef + abkdef) \qquad (6\text{-}54)$$

Replacing the transmittances by their values gives:

$$\frac{i_2}{e_1} = \frac{\theta L}{L^2 p^2 + Lp(R_e + 2R) + (R^2 + RR_e + \theta^2 L^2)} \qquad (6\text{-}55)$$

In steady-state, the response of the machine is given by:

$$i_2 = \frac{\theta L e_1}{R^2 + RR_e + \dot\theta^2 L^2} \qquad (6\text{-}56)$$

The analog diagram of Fig. 6-25c is deduced directly from the graph of Fig. 6-25b.

6-3-9. Synchronous generator in steady-state. Fig. 6-26 represents a generalized machine connected to two mutually perpendicular sets of brushes which are shifted by an angle θ with respect to the

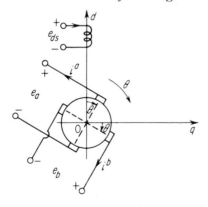

Fig. 6-26. Two-phase synchronous machine

axes $0d$ and $0q$. If it is supposed that this angle θ equals $t\dot{\theta}$, that is, if the brush axes rotates in the same direction and with the same velocity as the armature, the electromotive forces e_a and e_b which appear between these brushes will be sinusoidal and will have a phase shift of $90°$ between them. A two-phase generator (with fixed field and rotating armature) is thus obtained. The impedance flow graph of this machine will now be derived in the case of a steady-state operation. Because of the convention made earlier of a constant direction for the field, and with the condition assumed above that the field is constant with time, the armature field can also be considered constant. Thus, the currents in the various winding of the generalized machine will be direct currents.

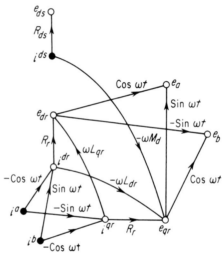

Fig. 6-27. Flow graph for the steady state operation of the two-phase synchronous machine

In Fig. 6–27, the impedance graph is drawn for the generalized machine, with three windings, ds, dr, and qr, by leaving out the terms in p. In addition, the brush rotation is introduced in the following manner: Let:

$$\theta = \omega t$$
$$\dot{\theta} = \omega \tag{6-57}$$

The armature currents can be decomposed along the two axes as:

$$i^{dr} = -i^a \cos \omega t + i^b \sin \omega t$$
$$i_{qr} = -i^a \sin \omega t - i^b \cos \omega t \tag{6-58}$$

The energy-balance equation gives:

$$e_a i^a + e_b i^b + e_{dr} i^{dr} + e_{qr} i^{qr} = 0 \qquad (6\text{-}59)$$

Replacing in the preceding equation the values of the currents i^{dr} and i^{qr} from Eq. (6-58), one obtains:

$$e_a = e_{dr} \cos \omega t + e_{qr} \sin \omega t$$
$$e_b = - e_{dr} \sin \omega t + e_{qr} \cos \omega t \qquad (6\text{-}60)$$

The linear Eqs. (6-58) and (6-60) are expressed on the graph of Fig. 6-27.

Reading directly from the graph:

$$e_a = - [R_r - \omega(L_{dr} - L_{qr}) \sin \omega t \cos \omega t] \, i^a$$
$$- \omega(L_{dr} \sin^2 \omega t + L_{qr} \cos^2 \omega t) i^b - (\omega M_d \sin \omega t) i^{ds}$$
$$e_b = \omega(L_{dr} \cos^2 \omega t + L_{qr} \sin^2 \omega t) i^a$$
$$- [R_r + \omega(L_{dr} - L_{qr}) \sin \omega t \cos \omega t] i^b - (\omega M_d \cos \omega t) i^{ds} \qquad (6\text{-}61)$$

Letting:

$$\frac{L_{dr} - L_{qr}}{2} = L_d$$
$$\frac{L_{dr} + L_{qr}}{2} = L_m \qquad (6\text{-}62)$$

the Eq. (6-60) becomes:

$$e_a = - (R_r - \omega L_d \sin 2\omega t) i^a - \omega(L_m - L_d \cos 2\omega t) i^b$$
$$- (\omega M_d \sin \omega t) i^{ds}$$
$$e_b = \omega(L_m + L_d \cos 2\omega t) i^a - (R_r + L_d \omega \sin 2\omega t) i^b$$
$$- (\omega M_d \cos \omega t) i^{ds} \qquad (6\text{-}63)$$

Suppose that the currents i^a and i^b are sinusoidal, and that i^b leads i^a by $\pi / 2$, then:

$$i^a = I \cos (\omega t + \alpha)$$
$$i^b = - I \sin (\omega t + \alpha) \qquad (6\text{-}64)$$

To represent the phasor diagram of this machine, one calculates:

$$E e^{j(\omega t + \varphi)} = e_a - j e_b \qquad (6\text{-}65)$$

This expression becomes:

$$E e^{j(\omega t + \varphi)} = - (R_r + jL_m \omega) I e^{j(\omega t + \alpha)} - jL_d \omega I e^{j(\omega t - \alpha)} + j\omega M_d i^{ds} e^{j\omega t} \qquad (6\text{-}66)$$

or:

$$j\omega M i^{ds} = E e^{j\varphi} + (R_r + jL_m \omega) I e^{j\alpha} + j L_d \omega I e^{-j\alpha} \qquad (6\text{-}67)$$

Eq. 6-67 corresponds to the phasor diagram of a synchronous generator with nonsaturated salient poles. This diagram is drawn in Fig. 6-28.

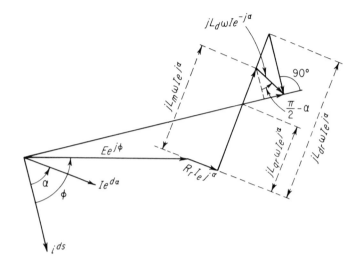

Fig. 6-28. Vector diagram for a salient pole synchronous machine

7

Algebraic Reduction of
Flow Graphs Using
A Digital Computer

7-1 INTRODUCTION

Flow graphs, which are obtained in a direct and automatic manner in all types of problems whose point of departure is a schematic diagram, can easily be introduced into the memory of a digital computer. The storage locations in the memory represent the nodes of the graph, numbered in a given order, and the contents of the words represent the branch transmittances. The reduction of a graph is essentially the calculation of residual transmittances, and it is easy to program this reduction for a computer. As seen in Chap. 1, the calculation of residual transmittances can be performed with a single reduction formula which is valid both for elementary transformations and for index reduction by loop elimination. One can thus program a digital computer to solve a flow graph.

181

In this chapter, the basis of a very general program for a linear algebraic reduction process is presented. This program can be used in problems where the coefficients have real or complex numerical values, or in problems whose coefficients are letters, algebraic operators, or functions of the complex variable $s = \sigma + j\omega$. The computer program for the reduction of a flow graph can also be used to perform operations on rectangular or square matrices, as well as matrix inversions.

Before describing the procedure of reduction of a flow graph by an automatic computer, it is necessary to generalize the definition of a flow graph given in the first chapter. More precisely, it is the correspondence between the graph and a system of linear equations that must be generalized. The topological operations that were performed on simple graphs acquire a broader significance in the case of generalized graphs. This permits a very general presentation of the reduction of a flow graph on a digital computer.

7-2   GENERALIZATION OF FLOW GRAPHS

7-2-1. Generalized graphs.   Just as the graphs of the preceding chapters represented the functional relationships between the variables of a problem, *the generalized graphs will represent some operational relationships between groups of variables.* As an example, in the graph of Fig. 7-1a, each variable that one wishes to represent is associated with a node, and the functional relationships become the branch transmittances. If the variables of the graph are grouped into the dotted rectangles, in order to define one source node, one sink node, and one internal node, the generalized graph of Fig. 7-1b is obtained. In this graph, each node represents a column matrix of node variables corresponding to the nodes inside a dotted section of the original graph. To each branch of the generalized graph is associated a matrix giving the relationships between the variables represented by the nodes at the extremities of that branch.

The generalized graphs are just as flexible in the representation of blocks of relationships between groups of variables, as are the simple graphs in the representation of systems of equations. No restrictions are placed upon the grouping of the variables; the nodes of the generalized graph do not all necessarily represent the same number of variables, and the matrices of this graph are generally rectangular. The variables can be grouped in any manner desired.

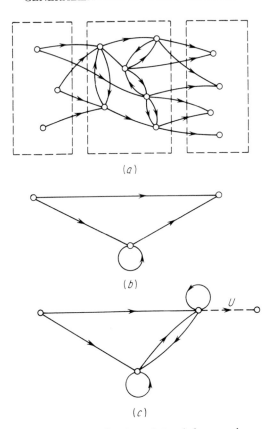

(a)

(b)

(c)

Fig. 7-1. Generalization of signal flow graphs

For example, instead of separating Fig. 7-1a into the dotted sections, it can be divided into an irregular checkerboard pattern. A generalized graph can then be drawn containing as many nodes as there are squares in the pattern. In addition to self-loops, the generalized graph contains a branch between each node for every group of branches affected by the preceding cutting. Thus, if in the detailed graph of Fig. 7-1a, the area of the central rectangle is reduced, and that of the right-hand rectangle is increased, the generalized graph of Fig. 7-1c results. On such a graph, it is always possible to add a branch of unit transmittance represented by the unit matrix U to show in explicit form a sink of the graph, as indicated by the dotted line. The graph of Fig. 7-1c thus represents at the sink node the sink node variables of the original graph and the node variables introduced into the right-hand rectangle by the new cutting.

It is evident that the generalized graph is not a residual graph, that is, a graph obtained by reduction of the initial graph, although a residual graph with the same topology as a generalized graph may exist for the same problem.

The same topology and the subsequent topological reductions will have very different significance, depending on whether these operations are performed on a simple graph or on a generalized one.

The generalization described above can also be applied to a generalized graph instead of to a detailed one. This means that in Fig. 7-1, the original graph could have been a generalized graph, and so the graph obtained in Fig. 7-1b would be a further generalization of an already generalized graph.

7-2-2. Reduction of generalized graphs. Topologically, transformations of generalized graphs are no different from those presented in the first chapter. The calculation of branch transmittances of the residual graph must, however, make use of the appropriate algebra.

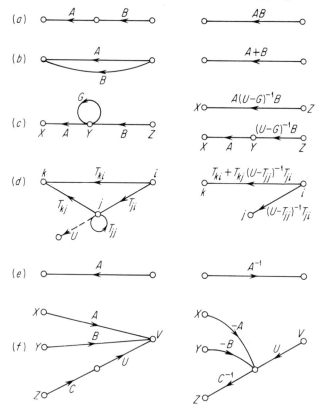

Fig. 7-2. Operations on generalized graphs

As an illustration the rules will be given for the reduction of generalized graphs which represent matrix equations. For convenience, the definitions and terminology of Chap. 1 are used; however, it will be more convenient in generalized graphs to follow the open paths backwards, that is, to follow the successive branches in the direction opposite to that indicated by the arrows, since then any noncommutative operators, such as matrices, would be written in their proper order. Also, in order to have the graph disposed in a manner such that the transmittances of a path appear in the same order as their factors appear when written out, it is best to orient the generalized graphs with the sinks at the left and the sources at the right.

The *elementary transformations* for two branches are shown in Figs. 7-2a and 7-2b. These transformations are sufficient for the reduction of a cascade graph. A proof of the *loop transformation* of Fig. 7-2c, can be obtained by writing the corresponding equations for the left-hand graph. If desired, it is possible to keep the middle node, as shown. Loop reduction can be effected only if there exists an inverse of the transmittance.

The elementary transformations and the loop reduction permit the elimination of any node *j*, of the graph by the *reduction formula:*

$$T'_{ki} = T_{ki} + T_{kj}(U - T_{jj})^{-1}T_{ji} \qquad (7\text{-}1)$$

where T'_{ki} is the new transmittance between nodes i and k. The application of this formula is illustrated in Fig. 7-2d, where a branch of unit transmittance is added (shown dotted), in order to keep all the variables of the initial graph in the reduced one.

With the reduction formula, it is always possible to reduce a graph of any order. The elementary transformations suffice to reduce the graph to an index-residual one, and after that the absorption of a node reduces the index by one each time. The final graph will be a cascade graph in which the variables of the sink nodes are explicitly expressed as functions of the sources. This is the only method for reducing the generalized graph since Mason's rule is obviously inapplicable.

The direct application of the reduction formula in Eq. (7-1) can be replaced by the following two steps, for any node:

1. If there is a self-loop at this node, it can be eliminated by multiplication of all incoming branch transmittances by the inverse of the return difference of the self-loops.

2. This node is then reduced to a sink, by removal, one by one, of the outgoing branches by calculating the residual transmittances passing through this node.

This single rule, consisting of the removal of all outgoing branches of nodes other than sources (starting with the self-loop) leads to a solution of any graph. The reduction is complete when a graph containing only sources and sinks is obtained. All the graphs obtained by application of this rule will be called equivalent, since all the nodes of the initial graph are retained at each stage and always represent the same variables. For example, starting with the graph of Fig. 7-2d (without drawing the dotted branch), the equivalent graph drawn on the right-hand side is derived, by removing, one by one, the branches leaving the node j, starting with the loop. *The application of the reduction formula in a digital computer comprises these two steps: elimination of self-loop and reduction of a node to a sink.*

It is sometimes possible to invert an open path. *Branch inversion,* as indicated in Fig. 7-2e, is possible only if the transmittance is a square matrix, and if its inverse exists. If this condition is met for all the branches of an open path, it can be inverted. The inversion can be performed in the manner described for simple graphs in Chapt. 1. It is always possible to separate a branch into two cascade branches, one of which has a unit transmittance; in this case, the inversion of a path can be represented as shown in Fig. 7-2f.

7-3 THE PROGRAMMING OF THE REDUCTION PROCESS

7-3-1. Use of the reduction formula. The reduction program for a flow graph will now be described using a generalized graph; it is evident that the same program will apply to a simple graph. This program is based exclusively on the repeated use of the reduction formula (in steps as previously described), by which any graph can be reduced to a residual graph showing only sources and sinks. As an illustration, consider the reduction in successive steps of the graph of Fig. 7-3a. This graph corresponds to the equations:

$$\begin{bmatrix} X \\ Y \\ Z \end{bmatrix} = \begin{bmatrix} U & 0 & 0 \\ A & B & C \\ D & E & F \end{bmatrix} \begin{bmatrix} X \\ Y \\ Z \end{bmatrix} \tag{7-2}$$

The reduction can start at any node; take node Z for example. There exists a self-loop at this node and it can be removed by trans-

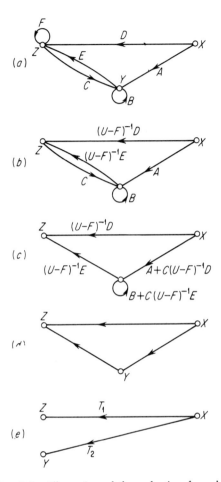

Fig. 7-3. Illustration of the reduction formula

forming the transmittances of the branches which converge toward it (Fig. 7-3b). The graph is then reduced to a graph in which node Z is a sink. This operation requires only the calculation of residual transmittances through this node in the preceding graph. Only the elementary transformations enter into this operation. The graph of Fig. 7-3c indicates the residual graph after one complete cycle of the reduction formula.

It suffices to repeat this cycle as many times as necessary in order to express all the variables directly in terms of the independent variables. In the example of Fig. 7-3, one more cycle is required (Figs. 7-3d and 7-3e). The final graph corresponds to the solution:

$$\begin{bmatrix} X \\ Y \\ Z \end{bmatrix} = \begin{bmatrix} U & 0 & 0 \\ T_1 & 0 & 0 \\ T_2 & 0 & 0 \end{bmatrix} \begin{bmatrix} X \\ Y \\ Z \end{bmatrix} \qquad (7\text{-}3)$$

where:

$$T_1 = (U - F)^{-1}D + (U - F)^{-1}ET_2$$
$$T_2 = [U - B - C(U - F)^{-1}E]^{-1}[A + C(U - F)^{-1}D]$$

The reduction can start at any node, and the nodes can be taken in any order. If these operations are programmed for a digital computer, a looped program results which must be run through m times for the reduction of m nodes. The loop of the program corresponds to one cycle of application of the reduction rule in Eq. (7-1) which is done in two steps: elimination of a self-loop, and reduction of a node. This program is represented schematically in Fig. 7-4. Naturally, only the internal nodes should be reduced, the source and sink nodes being excluded from the reduction process.

7-2-3. Inversion rules. In addition to the reduction rule, the

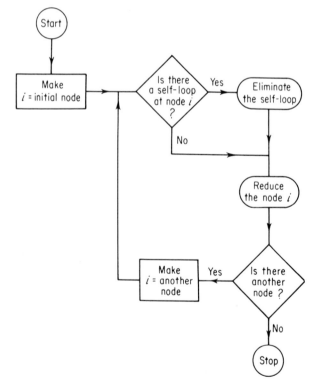

Fig. 7-4. Flow chart of a program of flowgraph reduction

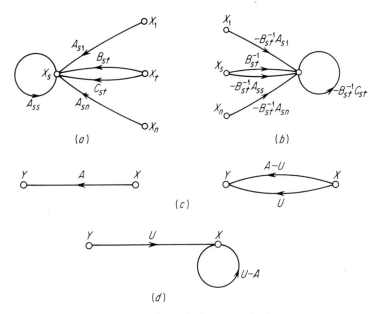

Fig. 7-5. Inversion rule for generalized graphs

general reduction program for a flow graph must include an inversion routine, or else it is necessary to put the graph into the computer in such a way that the reduction of the graph automatically produces the required inversion. In Fig. 7-2, an inversion rule is already given for the generalized graphs; it will suffice to modify this rule slightly in order to satisfy the foregoing objective.

Fig. 7-5a illustrates the generalized graph corresponding to the equations:

$$X_s = \sum_j A_{sj} X_j \qquad (7\text{-}4)$$

with branch A_{st} represented by two parallel branches:

$$A_{st} = B_{st} + C_{st} \qquad (7\text{-}5)$$

The path X_s-X_t through branch B_{st} can be inverted using the preceding rule to produce the graph of Fig. 7-5b, corresponding to the equation:

$$X_t = B_{st}^{-1}(X_s - C_{st}X_t - \sum_{j \neq t} A_{sj}X_j) \qquad (7\text{-}6)$$

If the transmittance C_{st} is zero ($A_{st} = B_{st}$), this is the inversion presented previously, corresponding to the equation:

$$X_t = B_{st}^{-1}(X_s - \sum_{j \neq t} A_{sj}X_j) \qquad (7\text{-}7\text{a})$$

But if B_{st} is equal to the unit matrix (and $C_{st} = A_{st} - U$), the following equation results:

$$X_t = X_s - (A_{st} - U)X_t - \sum_{j \neq t} A_{sj}X_j \qquad (7\text{-}7b)$$

In this form, the inversion of an open path does not imply an immediate inversion of any transmittance, whereas the inversion of Eq. (7-7a) requires the inversion of each of the branches of the open path considered. The reduction method just described will automatically produce the desired inversion, if the graph is first transformed by inversion on the branches of unit transmittance. If such branches do not appear in the initial graph, they can be easily introduced by drawing two parallel branches (one of which has a unit transmittance) to replace an initial branch of the graph. Such a substitution is indicated on the Fig. 7-5c, and the inversion corresponding to Eq. (7-7b) is represented in Fig. 7-5d.

7-3-3. Outline of a general program. The graph reduction procedure has been presented using a generalized graph, and a flow diagram of the reduction program is shown in Fig. 7-4. Such a program is as applicable to a generalized graph as to a simple graph, using transmittances that are numbers, or rational functions of the complex variable, $s = \sigma + j\omega$.

The first step of this program is the transcription of the graph into the computer memory. To this end, the nodes of the graph are numbered in the following order: the source nodes from 1 to k, the internal nodes from $k + 1$ to p, and the sink nodes from $p + 1$ to q. By placing these numbers along an axis (Fig. 7-6), it is possible to

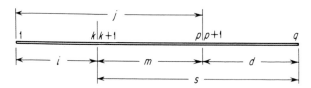

Fig. 7-6. The ordering of the nodes of the graph

define three segments which span all possible values of the indices i, s, and j, of the following equations corresponding to the generalized graph of Fig. 7-1b:

$$V_i = V_i$$
$$V_s = \sum_j M_{sj}V_j \qquad (7\text{-}8)$$

To insert the graph into the memory of the computer, it is first necessary to relate the memory addresses to the indices of the graph nodes. If each of the transmittances requires only one word of the memory, they can be inserted directly into the above-mentioned addresses. If, on the other hand, each transmittance requires more than one word (such as in the case of a generalized graph), the addresses will contain only a code word, which will give the address of the memory block where the transmittances can be found. The program can by itself take care of this eventuality, if a code word is used to specify beforehand the type of graph to be solved. It is necessary also to specify the number of sources k, and the number of sinks $d = (q - p)$.

The flow diagram of Fig. 7-4 becomes the main part of a general program of algebraic reduction, since it was developed for a generalized graph. Whatever the type of graph, whatever the nature of the transmittances, this program ensures the reduction of the graph. The reduction loop is run through m times for a graph of m internal nodes, until a residual graph is obtained containing only sources and sinks. According to the code word specifying the type of graph, the program will use particular sub-routines for the operations indicated by an ellipse in Fig. 7-4. If the transmittances are themselves flow graphs, these subroutines will behave as new programs which may require further subroutines. The master program for these will evidently be the same, since it is still a process of graph reduction. With a list of appropriate subroutines, the general program can reduce any graph whose transmittances are: matrices with numerical elements, or rational functions of the frequency s, or symbols representing submatrices or operators. Depending on the case, the results will appear in the form of a numerical answer, or an analytic expression.

For optimum programming, the graph structure must be considered to determine the most convenient order for the reduction of internal nodes, and also to ascertain that the graph is of such a form that the reduction can be done in an efficient manner. These two points will be briefly discussed.

By using the generalized graph, a very condensed graph can be drawn for a given problem. In this case, the reduction program must use several subprograms in order to pass from the transmittance in the original graph to the subgraph representing this transmittance, thence to the transmittances of the subgraph, which themselves in turn can be represented by other subgraphs. For such problems, it is sometimes possible to transform the initial graph in order to accelerate this process. As a simple illustration, consider a graph whose transmittances are complex coefficients:

$$C_{ik} = a_{ik} + jb_{ik} \tag{7-9}$$

which are related to variables that are themselves complex:

$$Z_k = x_k + jy_k \tag{7-10}$$

a branch can be represented as in Fig. 7-7a, which can be thought of as a generalized graph, where the nodes represent the column matrix of the real and imaginary parts of Z, and where the transmittances are the matrices:

$$C_{ik} = \begin{bmatrix} a_{ik} & -b_{ik} \\ b_{ik} & a_{ik} \end{bmatrix} \tag{7-11}$$

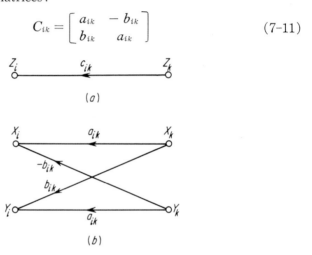

(a)

(b)

Fig. 7-7. Two flow graph representations of the same equations

It is also possible to separate the nodes of this graph and to draw a simple graph whose branches will have real transmittances, as in Fig. 7-7b. It will be up to the programmer to judge which type of graph is most appropriate to a particular case, since the above-mentioned reduction program can solve graphs of either type.

The order in which the internal nodes are absorbed can be random. It may occur, however, that the reduction of one node produces several residual transmittances which must be reduced in succeeding steps. A different order could reduce the number of operations in the reduction of the graph. The optimum order of reduction of the internal nodes evidently depends on the structure of the graph, and a reasonable solution will suggest itself to someone who has done several reductions. The programmer can account for this himself by establishing a suitable ordering of the reduction of the internal nodes, or else the program can contain as an additional step a general examination of the graph structure, in order that the computer can determine an appropriate sequence.

7-4 SIMPLE EXAMPLE OF REDUCTION PROGRAM

7-4-1. Description. In order to exemplify the methods presented in this chapter, a program has been written for the reduction of a simple graph, whose transmittances are real numbers. Such a program performs the operations indicated in Fig. 7-4 without requiring subroutines, since the elimination of a self-loop and the reduction of a node are simple operations of division or addition. The program as described can thus perform the algebraic operations of matrix algebra (as long as the coefficients are real numbers), perform matrix inversions, and so on, as well as solve the loop equations of a network for the input and transfer admittances, having been given only the incidence matrix and the matrix of the branch impedances of the network.

In this particular program, the number of variables must not exceed a maximum fixed number. These variables correspond to the nodes of the graph and are numbered as indicated in Fig. 7-6. First, the numbers of the source nodes and sink nodes are entered into the computer, along with the branch transmittances. The transmittances can be represented inside the memory as in a rectangular grid (Fig. 7-8). The squares are identified by the order number of their row i and column j such that the transmittances a_{ij} of the graph occupies the square ij. Using the symbols of Fig. 7-6, a rectangle of the grid can be associated with the internal nodes. The group of

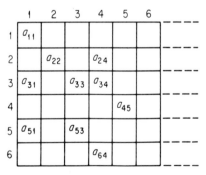

Fig. 7-8. The transmittances of the graph as visualized in the memory of a digital computer

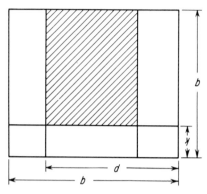

Fig. 7-9. Allocation of transmittances in the computer memory

squares so allocated is shaded in the diagram of Fig. 7-9. The reduction program is not optimum: the nodes are transformed by proceeding from column to column in Fig. 7-9, starting by the internal node of the highest order (node p).

In this representation, self-loops correspond to the squares on the diagonal of the grid. These loops will be reduced by dividing all the elements of a line by one minus the diagonal term.

After each loop elimination, the node corresponding to the column where this loop is located is reduced. Take for example column j; in order to reduce node j, each term of index kj is multiplied by the terms of index $j1$, $j2$, ... of line j, and these are added to the elements of index $k1$, $k2$, ... of line k.

These two operations have the effect of transforming node j of the graph into a sink, according to the reduction formula in Eq. (7-1). The reduction is complete when there are no more nonzero terms in the shaded portion of Fig. 7-9. The process leads to a residual graph containing only source nodes (from 1 to k) and sinks ($k + 1$ to q).

7-4-2. Program for the IBM 650. The program described above has been coded for the IBM 650 computer. This program can accommodate as many as 40 variables and requires about 350 orders. Most of the memory (2,000 words) is used for the numerical values of the transmittances. For testing purposes, several problems have been solved with this program such as: solution of a simple graph, solution of potentials in a uniform grid, and matrix inversion. The inversion of a 10 by 10 test matrix was done in 35 seconds.

7-4-3. Program for the ALWAC III-E. Using the Alwac III-E, which has no built-in "floating point" unit, the program of Sec.

7-4-1 was coded in two ways, in order to permit solution in "fixed point" or in "floating point." This computer has a two-level memory; a slow memory of 256 channels of 32 words each, and a working memory of 128 words. Transfer from the slow memory to the rapid memory, or vice-versa, is done in blocks of 32 words and requires around 100 milliseconds. Because of this particular memory structure, the program was written to treat a maximum of 32 variables. As a test, it was used to perform the inversion of a 16 by 16 matrix. The calculation was done in 7 and 1/2 minutes, using "floating point."

A Rule for the Expansion

of the

Graph Determinant

1. Expansion of a determinant with respect to its excess terms.
Consider a matrix C in which a coefficient c_{ij} is decomposed into a
sum of two terms $(a_{ij} + b_{ij})$. This decomposition is necessary in
order to formulate the expansion of the determinant in terms of the
bidirectional graph. By determinant theory:

$$
\begin{vmatrix}
c_{11} & c_{12} & \cdot & c_{1n} \\
c_{21} & \cdot & \cdot & c_{2n} \\
\cdot & \cdot & \cdot & \cdot \\
\cdot & \cdot & (a_{ij}+b_{ij}) & \cdot \\
\cdot & \cdot & \cdot & \cdot \\
c_{n1} & c_{n2} & \cdot & c_{nn}
\end{vmatrix}
$$

$$
=
\begin{vmatrix}
c_{11} & \cdot & 0 & c_{1n} \\
c_{21} & \cdot & 0 & c_{2n} \\
\cdot & \cdot & 0 & \cdot \\
\cdot & \cdot & a_{ij} & \cdot \\
\cdot & \cdot & 0 & \cdot \\
c_{n1} & c_{n2} & 0 & c_{nn}
\end{vmatrix}
+
\begin{vmatrix}
c_{11} & \cdot & c_{1j} & c_{1n} \\
c_{21} & \cdot & c_{2j} & c_{2n} \\
\cdot & \cdot & \cdot & \cdot \\
c_{i1} & \cdot & b_{ij} & c_{in} \\
\cdot & \cdot & \cdot & \cdot \\
c_{n1} & c_{n2} & c_{nj} & c_{nn}
\end{vmatrix}
\qquad (1)
$$

If Δ denotes the determinant of the matrix C, and Δ_{ij} the minor obtained by removing row i and column j, and $\Delta^{a_{ij}}$ the determinant when the term a_{ij} is zero, the preceding formula can be rewritten as:

$$\Delta = a_{ij}\Delta_{ij} + \Delta^{a_{ij}} \qquad (2)$$

The first term on the right of Eq. (2) comes from the Laplace expansion of the first determinant on the right of Eq. (1). The last term in Eq. (2) can be evaluated in the same manner by decomposing another element c_{km} into two terms $(a_{km} + b_{km})$ so as to obtain:

$$\Delta^{a_{ij}} = a_{km}\Delta^{a_{ij}}_{km} + \Delta^{a_{ij}a_{km}} \qquad (3)$$

Let $\Delta_{ij, \, km, \, rp, \, \cdots \, qn}$ designate the minor obtained by removing the rows $i, k, r, \cdots q$ and the columns $j, m, p, \cdots n$, and let $\Delta^{a_{ij}a_{km}a_{rp}\cdots a_{qn}}$ designate the determinant calculated after having cancelled the terms $a_{ij}, a_{km}, a_{rp}, \cdots a_{qn}$. By successive application of the preceding procedure, the following expression for the determinant of the matrix C is obtained:

$$\Delta = a_{ij}\Delta_{ij} + a_{km}\Delta^{a_{ij}}_{km} + a_{rp}\Delta^{a_{ij}a_{km}}_{rp} + \cdots + \Delta^{a_{ij}a_{km}a_{rp}\cdots a_{qn}} \qquad (4)$$

There are $(n-1)$ terms in the preceding equation if n elements are decomposed in the initial matrix, and each of the right hand determinants is of degree $(n-1)$ except the last which is of degree n. However, since the choice of a_{ij} is arbitrary, the last determinant can always be made zero by choosing the a_{ij} in the following manner:

$$a_{ij} = \sum_{k=1}^{n} c_{ik} \qquad (5)$$

or:

$$a_{ij} = \sum_{k=1}^{n} c_{kj} \qquad (6)$$

The last determinant of Eq. (4) is thus zero, since it is the determinant of a matrix whose elements add up to zero for any row or column.

The terms a_{ij} defined in the Eqs. (5) and (6) are called "row excesses" and "column excesses." A group of particularly interesting excesses are those obtained from the principal diagonal, which will be called "diagonal excesses." These are defined with respect to the rows:

$$a_{ii} = \sum_{k=1}^{n} c_{ik} \qquad (7)$$

or to the columns:

$$a_{ii} = \sum_{k=1}^{n} c_{ki} \qquad (8)$$

When the node or the loop equations are written for a network with the voltages chosen with respect to a reference node, or with the loop currents defined in the meshes of a planar network, the diagonal excesses represent admittances or impedances of branches of this network. In the indefinite bidirectional graph, the diagonal excesses will thus appear as branch transmittances. More specifically, they are the coefficients of the branches attached to that node of the graph which must be removed to render the graph definite. In a nonreciprocal network, the two coefficients associated with the two arrows of a branch of the bidirectional graph represent the diagonal excesses, which are taken relative to a row and to a column respectively.

Eq. (4) can be written in terms of the diagonal excesses as follows:

$$\Delta = a_{11}\Delta_{11} + a_{22}\Delta_{22}^{a_{11}} + a_{33}\Delta_{33}^{a_{11}a_{22}} + \dots + \Delta^{a_{11}a_{22}\dots a_{nn}} \tag{9a}$$

To simplify the notation, ij only will be used instead of a_{ij} as upper indices, and since both upper and lower indices appear doubled, only one index of each pair will be written. With this change of notation, Eq. (9a) becomes:

$$\Delta = a_1\Delta_1 + a_2\Delta_2^1 + a_3\Delta_3^{12} + a_4\Delta_4^{123} + \dots + \Delta^{123\dots n} \tag{9b}$$

The order in which the excesses appear in this expansion is not important; it must be noted, however, that the upper index of any given term must contain all the indices of the preceding factors. Depending on whether the row excesses or column excesses are used, two different expansions can be written if the matrix C is not symmetrical. The last term is zero, as explained before. In the case of a symmetrical matrix, this last term is the determinant of an indefinite matrix as defined by Shekel[23].

Any determinant in the Eq. (9b) is called a cofactor. Any cofactor is itself a function of the excesses a_j that appear as factors in the terms that come after this cofactor. To obtain an expansion where these a_j are completely factored out, it is necessary to expand further the factors already obtained. For example:

$$\Delta_1 = a_2\Delta_{12} + \Delta_1^2$$
$$\Delta_1^2 = a_3\Delta_{13}^2 + \Delta_1^{23}$$

or again:

$$\Delta_2^1 = a_3\Delta_{23}^1 + \Delta_2^{13}$$

By expanding in this manner, all the cofactors of Eq. (9b), a formula is obtained in which the a_j appear only as factors, in all possible combinations, n at a time, $(n-1)$ at a time, and so on. Each of these factors is multiplied by a determinant which no longer depends on a_j. For example, a third order matrix will give:

$$\Delta = a_1 a_2 a_3 + a_1 a_2 \Delta_{12}^3 + a_1 a_3 \Delta_{13}^2 + a_2 a_3 \Delta_{23}^1 + a_1 \Delta_1^{23} + a_2 \Delta_2^{13} + a_3 \Delta_3^{12} \quad (10)$$

The upper indices of the cofactors signify that the corresponding excesses must be nulled to calculate the cofactors. The upper indices are no longer necessary if the expansion formula is written with all the diagonal excesses factored out. In any case, these indices can easily be found by remembering that the n indices always appear together with any Δ in Eq. (10). Omitting the upper indices, the determinant of a matrix of order n can thus be written in a simpler way:

$$\Delta = \sum a_i \Delta_i + \sum a_i a_j \Delta_{ij} + \sum a_i a_j a_k \Delta_{ijk} + \dots + (a_1 a_2 a_3 \dots a_n) \quad (11)$$

The lower indices of $\Delta_{ij\dots}$ signify that the cofactors are calculated after having removed the rows and columns $i, j, \dots$ from the initial matrix. These determinants are therefore of order $(n - k)$ where k is the number of indices, and they can be evaluated by reapplying Eq. (11) after having, once again, defined the diagonal excesses of a reduced matrix.

As an example, the determinant of the matrix C below, in which the excesses are underlined, will be evaluated.

$$C = \begin{vmatrix} \underline{a_1} + b_2 + b_3 & -b_3 & -b_2 \\ -b_3 & \underline{a_2} + b_3 + b_1 & -b_1 \\ -b_2 & -b_1 & \underline{a_3} + b_1 + b_2 \end{vmatrix}$$

The determinant can be written as:

$$\Delta = a_1 a_2 a_3 + a_1 a_2 (b_1 + b_2) + a_1 a_3 (b_1 + b_3) + a_2 a_3 (b_2 + b_3)$$
$$+ a_1 \begin{vmatrix} b_3 + b_1 & -b_1 \\ -b_1 & b_1 + b_2 \end{vmatrix} + a_2 \begin{vmatrix} b_2 + b_3 & -b_2 \\ -b_2 & b_1 + b_2 \end{vmatrix}$$
$$+ a_3 \begin{vmatrix} b_2 + b_3 & -b_3 \\ -b_3 & b_3 + b_1 \end{vmatrix}$$

The cofactors of order 1 have been expanded in the preceding expression; the cofactors of order 2 will now be evaluated by using Eq. (11) in the determinants shown below, in which the underlined terms define the new excesses.

$$\begin{vmatrix} \underline{b_3} + b_1 & -b_1 \\ -b_1 & b_1 + \underline{b_2} \end{vmatrix} = b_3 b_2 + b_3 (b_1) + b_2 (b_1)$$

$$\begin{vmatrix} b_2 + \underline{b_3} & -b_2 \\ -b_2 & \underline{b_1} + b_2 \end{vmatrix} = b_1 b_3 + b_1 (b_2) + b_3 (b_2)$$

$$\begin{vmatrix} b_2 + b_3 & -b_3 \\ -b_3 & b_3 + b_1 \end{vmatrix} = b_1 b_2 + b_1(b_3) + b_2(b_3)$$

The C matrix of this example corresponds to the bidirectional graph of Fig. 1 whose indefinite matrix is:

$$C = \begin{bmatrix} a_1 + b_2 + b_3 & -b_3 & -b_2 & -a_1 \\ -b_3 & a_2 + b_3 + b_1 & -b_1 & -a_2 \\ -b_2 & -b_1 & a_3 + b_1 + b_2 & -a_3 \\ -a_1 & -a_2 & -a_3 & a_1 + a_2 + a_3 \end{bmatrix}$$

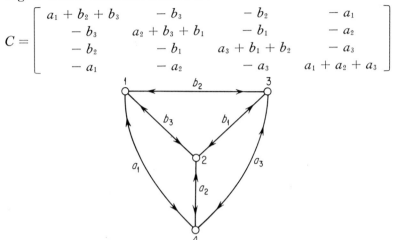

Fig. 1. Example of a bidirectional graph

It should be noted that the excesses appear as coefficients of the branches that are attached to node 4, the node that was removed to make the graph definite. The determinants of orders 1 and 2 are calculated in subgraphs which no longer contain the branches a_i. It is therefore possible to interpret Eq. (11) as a series of operations on the graph.

2. *Determinant of the Bidirectional Graph.* The indefinite bidirectional graph corresponds to the indefinite matrix in which the rows and columns add up to zero. For example, the following indefinite admittance matrix corresponds to the graph of Fig. 2a:

$$Y_i = \begin{bmatrix} c_{12} + c_{13} + c_{14} & -c_{12} & -c_{13} & -c_{14} \\ -c_{21} & c_{21} + c_{23} + c_{24} & -c_{23} & -c_{24} \\ -c_{31} & -c_{32} & c_{31} + c_{32} + c_{34} & -c_{34} \\ -c_{41} & -c_{42} & -c_{43} & c_{41} + c_{42} + c_{43} \end{bmatrix}$$

In order to obtain a definite matrix (by the choice of a reference node in the network), it is necessary to remove from the matrix Y_i one row and a corresponding column. In the definite matrix Y, the diagonal excesses can be defined with respect to rows or to columns. For example, from the matrix Y_i the following definite matrix is obtained by choosing node 4 as reference node:

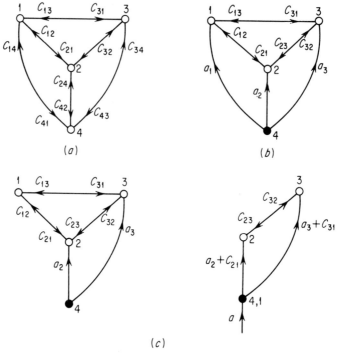

Fig. 2. Expansion of a bidirectional graph

$$Y = \begin{bmatrix} c_{12} + c_{13} + \underline{c_{14}} & -c_{12} & -c_{13} \\ -c_{21} & c_{21} + c_{23} + \underline{c_{24}} & -c_{23} \\ -c_{31} & -c_{32} & c_{31} + c_{32} + \underline{c_{34}} \end{bmatrix}$$

The underlined terms are the diagonal excesses relative to the rows, and these excesses are the coefficients of the branches that diverge from node 4 in the graph of Fig. 2a. The diagonal excesses relative to the columns could just as well have been chosen; these would correspond to the branches directed towards the reference node.

If one considers a symmetrical minor obtained from Y by removing one or more rows or columns, a new matrix is obtained which can also be made indefinite. This indefinite matrix corresponds to an indefinite bidirectional graph which is a subgraph of the initial one. The new diagonal excesses appear in the subgraph in the same manner as in the preceding case.

It is therefore possible to interpret the expansion of the determinant as a series of operations performed on the indefinite graph, or on the subgraphs obtained by removing certain nodes and the branches attached to these nodes. The first operation consists in identifying the excesses in terms of which the expansion will be made.

This step is represented in Fig. 2b where node 4, which was chosen as reference node, 'is darkened. A single arrow appears on the branches connected to this node and it is this arrow which is associated with the row excess. These excesses are designated by a_i in order to be able to apply the preceding formulas directly.

The basic formula of the expansion is in Eq. (2) in which one excess is factored out. In the language of graphs, this operation consists of establishing two subgraphs: the first is the initial graph with the branch of coefficient a_{ij} removed; the second is obtained from the initial graph by "factoring" a_{ij} by superposition of the node at the extremity of a_{ij} and of the reference node. Fig. 2c indicates this operation for a_1, the first diagonal excess (the row excess $a_1 = c_{14}$). Eqs. (3) and (4) can be interpreted in the same manner by expanding a graph into two subgraphs at each step.

Operating in this manner on any graph, any coefficient in the expression of the determinant can always be factored. If a complete expansion of the determinant is desired in terms of all the excesses (Eq. 11), it is not necessary to repeat several times on the graph the operation already described, since the subgraph corresponding to a given term of the expansion can easily be found. This subgraph is obtained from the original graph by removing the branches having the coefficients a_i, and by superimposing on the reference node the nodes at the extremeties of the a_i which appear as factors of the desired term. The determinant is written directly from the graph:

1. by choosing a reference node and suppressing the arrows that are directed toward this node, to define a group of a_i,
2. by writing the sum of products of a_i in all the possible combinations when taken one at a time, two at a time, and so on
3. by multiplying each of these terms by a cofactor which becomes the determinant of a subgraph described above. This determinant can be calculated by repeating the steps (1), (2) and (3) for the subgraph.

As an example, the determinant of the graph in Fig. 2a becomes:

$$
\begin{aligned}
\Delta = \; & a_1 a_2 a_3 \\
& + a_1 a_2 (c_{31} + c_{32}) \\
& + a_1 a_3 (c_{21} + c_{23}) \\
& + a_2 a_3 (c_{12} + c_{13}) \\
& + a_1 [c_{21} c_{31} + c_{21}(c_{32}) + c_{31}(c_{23})] \\
& + a_2 [c_{12} c_{32} + c_{12}(c_{31}) + c_{32}(c_{13})] \\
& + a_3 [c_{13} c_{23} + c_{13}(c_{21}) + c_{33}(c_{12})]
\end{aligned}
$$

It is not necessary to draw the different subgraphs to obtain the determinant. Although these subgraphs are obtained by successively removing the branches of the initial graph, it is nevertheless possible to see any particular subgraph by covering with the hand a part of the initial graph.

Since the indefinite graph corresponds to an indefinite matrix, any given node can be chosen as reference for the calculation of the determinant. This determinant is, in effect, a principal minor of the indefinite matrix, and it is known that all the principal minors of this type of matrix are equal. This knowledge is used to simplify the expansion of the determinant in a graph like that of a triode given in Fig. 3a. The expansion relative to the branches that emanate from node 3 will not contain the negative terms which might appear in a different expansion because of the coefficient $(b - g_m)$.

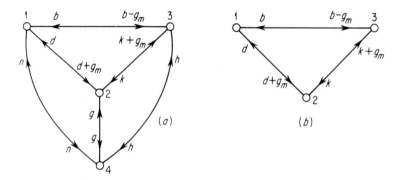

Fig. 3. Bidirectional graphs of triode amplifier

The initial graph is always indefinite, but this is not generally true of the subgraphs. However, the subgraph obtained by removing from any graph one node and branches is indefinite if the branches removed are reciprocal $(a_{ij} = a_{ji})$. Thus, the subgraph of Fig. 3b is an indefinite graph. This is a useful feature, since the principal minors of this subgraph are equal and can thus be calculated by using any node as reference. Thus, the determinant of the graph in Fig. 3a is readily obtained:

$$\Delta = ngh + ng(b + k) + nh(d + g_m + k) + gh(b + d)$$
$$+ (n + g + h)[bk + d(d + g_m) + kd]$$

The expansion is started by using node 4 as reference. The last three terms of the expansion (those in brackets) are equal and are calculated by using node 3 as reference.

The expansion formulas given in this appendix are valid for all indeterminate graphs whether of type N, M, or H.

3. *Conclusion.* In passive reciprocal networks, the determinant can be obtained from the topological graph by enumeration of all the trees and summation of the branch admittance products of each tree. The expansion formulas presented in this appendix allow a generalization of this method for nonreciprocal networks if a **"unidirectional tree"** is first defined, since it will be shown that the determinant for any network is the sum of the products of the coefficients of the branches of these unidirectional trees, drawn from the same node.

A unidirectional tree is a tree formed from the bidirectional graph, by taking only one of the arrows on each branch, such that all the arrows are in the same direction with respect to some node, which will be called the **"tree root."** The branches of this tree are thus either all directed towards this root or else away from it.

When calculating the determinant of the bidirectional graph by repeated applications of Eq. (11), all the unidirectional trees that have the same root are enumerated. Inversely, the determinant can be obtained by enumerating all the unidirectional trees having the same root, and by summing the coefficient products associated with the arrows on these trees. As an example, the determinant of Fig. 3b can be obtained using the unidirectional trees drawn in Fig. 4.

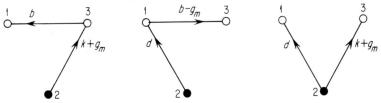

Fig. 4. Unidirectional trees with node 2 as a root

The unidirectional trees were drawn with node 2 as a root, and all arrows are directed away from it. From the preceding section, it is known that the same result could be obtained by taking the opposite direction on the branches, or by using any other node as a root.

The number of unidirectional trees of a graph will generally equal the number of ordinary trees; however, if the network contains a unilateral element the corresponding branch will have only one arrow. In such cases, the number of unidirectional trees could be less than the number of regular trees of the graph.

References

1. Kron, G., *Tensor Analysis of Networks* (John Wiley and Sons Inc., New York 1939).
2. Tustin, A., "Direct Current Machines for Control Systems" (*E. Q. F. N. Spon Ltd*, London, 1952 p. 46).
3. Mason, S. J., "Feedback Theory: Some Properties of Signal Flow Graphs" (*Proc. Inst. Radio Engrs.*, **41** September 1953, pp. 1144–1156).
4. Trent, H. M., "Isomorphisms Between Oriented Linear Graphs and Lumped Physical Systems" (*J. acoust. Soc. Amer.* **27** May 1955, pp. 500–527).
5. Firestone, F. A., "The Mobility Method of Computing the Vibrations of Linear Mechanical and Acoustical Systems: Mechanical-Electrical Analogies" (*J. appl. Phys.* **9** June 1938, pp. 373–387).
6. Linvill, W. K., "System Theory as an Extension of Circuit Theory" (*Inst. Radio Engrs.*, *Trans.* **CT-3** No. 4, December 1956, pp. 217–223).
7. Linvill, W. K., "Signal Theory Issue" (*Inst. Radio Engrs.*, *Trans.* **CT-3** No. 4, December 1956, pp. 206–289).
8. Bode, H. W., *Network Analysis and Feedback Amplifiers Design* (Van Nostrand Co., Inc., New York 1945).
9. Happ, W. W., "Dynamic Characteristics of Four-Terminal Networks" (*Convention Record of the Inst. Radio Engrs.*, 1954, pp. 60–76).
10. Mason, S. J., "Feedback Theory: Further Properties of Signal Flow Graphs" (*Proc. Inst. Radio Engrs.*, **44** July 1956, pp. 920–926).
11. Lorens, C. S., "A Proof of the Non-Intersecting Loop Rule for

the Solution of Linear Equations by Flow Graphs" (Massachusetts Inst. Technol., Res. Lab. Electron., *Quarterly Progress Report* No. 40, January 1956, pp. 97–102).

12. Boisvert, M., and Robichaud, L. P. A., "Direct Analysis of Electrical Networks" (*Research Report No. 9*, Electrical Engineering Dept., Laval University, October 1956).

13. Truxal, J. G., *Control System Synthesis* (McGraw-Hill Book Co., Inc., New York 1955).

14. Bayard, M., "Théorie des réseaux de Kirchhoff, Régime sinusoïdal et synthèse" (Collection technique et scientifique du C.N.E.T. Editions de la revue d'optique, Paris, 1954).

15. Foster, R. M., "Topologic and Algebraic Considerations in Network Synthesis" (*Proc. Symp. Mod. Network Synthesis,* Polytechnic Institute of Brooklyn 1952).

16. Synge, J.L., "The Fundamental Theorem of Electrical Networks" (*Quart. appl. Math.*, 9 July 1951, pp. 113–127, 11 July 1953, pp. 215–219).

17. Roth, J.P., "An Application of Algebraic Topology to Numerical Analysis: On the Existence of a Solution to the Network Problem" (*Proc. nat. Acad. Sci.*, 41 July 1955, pp. 518–521).

18. Lorens, C.S., "Basic Theory of Flow Graphs: Inversion" (Massachusetts Inst. Technol., Res. Lab. Electron., *Quarterly Progress Report* No. 41, April 1956).

19. Wing, O., "Ladder Network Analysis by Signal Flow Graphs: Application to Analog Computer Programming" (*Inst. Radio Engrs. Trans.*, CT-3 December 1956, pp. 289–294).

20. Robichaud, L. P. A., "Study of Physical Systems through Signal Flow Graph" (Doctoral dissertation (in preparation), Electrical Engineering Dept., Laval University).

21. Ku, Y. H., "Résumé of Maxwell's and Kirchhoff's Rules for Network Analysis" (J. Franklin Inst., 253 March 1952, pp. 211–224).

22. Percival, W. S., "The Solution of Passive Electrical Networks by means of Mathematical Trees" (*Proc. Instn Elect Engrs.*, May 1953, Part III, 100, pp. 143–150).

23. Shekel, J., "Voltage Reference Node: Its Transformation in Nodal Analysis" (*Wireless Engr.*, 31 January 1954, pp. 6–10).

24. Whitney, H., "Non-Separable and Planar Graphs" (*Trans. Amer. Math. Soc.*, 34 1932, pp. 339–362).

25. Bloch, A., "On Methods for the Construction of Networks Dual to Non-Planar Networks" (*Proc. Phys. Soc.*, 58 1946, p. 677).

26. Zadeh, L. A., "A Note on the Analysis of Vacuum Tube and Transistor Circuits" (*Proc. Inst. Radio. Engrs.*, 41 August 1953, pp. 989–992).

27. Tsang, N. F., "On Electrical Network Determinants" (*J. Math. Phys.*, **33** July 1954, pp. 185–193).
28. Cederbaum, I., "On Network Determinants" (*Proc. Inst. Radio Engrs.*, **44** February 1956, pp. 258–259).
29. Okada, S., "On Node and Mesh Determinants" (*Proc. Inst. Radio Engrs.*, **43** October 1955, p. 1527).
30. Guillemin, E. A., *Introductory Circuit Theory* (John Wiley and Sons, New York 1953).
31. Feldtkeller, R., and Strecker F., "Grundlagen der Theorie des Allgemeinen Vierpols" (*E. N. T.*, **6** 1929, pp. 93–112).
32. Baerwald, H. G., "Die Eigenschaften Symmetrischer 4n-Pole" (*Sitzb. d. Preuss. Akad. d. Wiss.* **33** 1931, pp. 784–829).
33. Breisig, F., "Über das Nebensprechen in Fernsprechkreisen" (*Elektrotech. Z.*, **42** 1921, p. 933–939).
34. Pritchard, R. S., "Electric Network Representation of Transistors—A Survey" (*Inst. Radio Engrs., Trans.* **CT-3** March 1956, pp. 5–22).
35. Tables of Chebyshev Polynomials (National Bureau of Standard, *Applied Mathematics Series* 9.19, December 1952).
36. Pantell, R. H., "Minimum-Phase Transfer-Function Synthesis" (*Inst. Radio Engrs., Trans.* **CT-2** June 1955, pp. 133–137).
37. Ho, E. C., "A General Matrix Factorization Method for Network Synthesis" (*Inst. Radio Engrs., Trans.* **CT-2** June 1955, pp. 146–153).
38. Kron, G., *Equivalent Circuits of Electrical Machinery* (John Wiley and Sons, New York 1951).
39. Robichaud, L. P. A., "A Study of Physical Systems Through Signal Flow Graphs" (Canadian Armament Research and Development Establishment, *Technical Memorandum*, 167/57).
    Part 1 "General Introduction" (in preparation).
    Part 2 "Direct Analysis of Electrical Networks" (January, 1959).
    Part 3 "Analysis of Quadripole and N-port Networks" (January 1960).
    Part 4 "Direct Simulation on Analog Computers" (January 1958).
    Part 5 "Axis Transformations" (in preparation).
    Part 6 "Generalized Flow Graph Reduction by Digital Computers" (in preparation).
40. Robichaud, L. P. A., "Direct Simulation on Analog Computers through Signal Flow Graphs" (Paper presented at the Canadian I. R. E. Convention Toronto, 2 October 1956).
41. Robichaud, L. P. A., "Direct Analysis of Electrical Networks through Signal Flow Graphs" (Canadian Convention Record of the I. R. E., 10 October 1958, pp. 344–354).

42. Deflandre, P., "Contribution à l'étude des Machines Electriques au moyen des diagrammes de transfert" (Master's Thesis presented at the Graduate School, Laval University, November 1959).

43. Coates, C. L., "Flow Graph Solutions of Linear Algebraic Equations" (*Inst. Radio Engrs., Trans.* **CT-6** June 1959, pp. 170–187).

44. Desoer, C. A., "The Optimum Formula for the Gain of a Flow Graph or a simple Derivation of Coates Formula" (*Proc. Inst. Radio Engrs.* **48** May 1960, pp. 883–889).

Index